PLINY'S NATURAL HISTORY

An Account by a Roman
of
What Romans Knew and Did and Valued

Compacted from the many volumes of the
HISTORIA NATURALIS

By
LOYD HABERLY
Fairleigh Dickinson University

FREDERICK UNGAR PUBLISHING CO.
NEW YORK

INTRODUCTION

The *Natural History* is what remains of the big shelf of
notebooks in which the elder Pliny wrote down everything
he saw or heard or read. It is a one-man encyclopedia of
about twenty thousand entries that tell us more concerning
the everyday Roman world than any and all other books
that have survived. Excerpted in large part from earlier
writers, it keeps alive some portion of almost two thousand
ancient volumes that we only know of because Pliny
quoted them.

The samplings that make this present book are fair
to Pliny in that they show his best judgment, as well as his
worst. He was a man of his time, and that time included
the Ministry of Christ. For these pages I have selected his
entries on the Roman customs and ideas and skills that most
interest us today. Nothing but his whole many-volumed
work can show the stature his incredible curiosity and industry attained. Those many volumes in complete transla-
tion are hard to come by, as they date from long ago. I
have used the Bohn edition of 1855.

In slightly modernizing the language and punctuation
of that edition, I have been generously assisted by Miss
Helen Tanzer who has written so competently on the villas
of the younger Pliny—our man's letter-writing nephew.
From her pen comes the following brief biography:

"Pliny the Elder was born in Verona in A.D. 23 in the
reign of Tiberius. He went to Rome for his education. As
an officer of cavalry he served in the army of Germany in
the reign of Claudius (48-52). When on leave he visited
neighboring provinces. He gave up his military career and
dedicated his life to science and literature (53-67). He was
made procurator of Hispania Citerior by Nero and held
that position under Nero, Galba, Otho, Vitellius and Vespasian. By this service he became eligible for admission to
the Equestrian Order. He was very proud of this promo-

tion. In 74 he was made an admiral and was put in charge of the fleet at Misenum, which accounts for his presence there at the time of the eruption of Vesuvius (79). He adopted his nephew in 73 and raised him to the Equestrian Order. He suffered from asthma and his nephew thought that this made him particularly susceptible to the fumes of the volcano which caused his death in 79."

The letter describing that eruption—which also brought an end to the lifetimes of Herculaneum and Pompeii—forms the final section of this book.

L. H.

Fairleigh Dickinson University
Rutherford, New Jersey

CONTENTS

THIS WORLD AND THE NEXT

What Is Man?

First attention is justly due to Man, for whose sake all other things appear to have been produced by Nature, though it is far from easy to determine whether she has proved to him a kind parent or a merciless stepmother.

In the first place, she obliges him alone, of all animated beings, to clothe himself while, to all the rest, she has given various kinds of coverings, such as shells, crusts, spines, hides, furs, bristles, hair, down, feathers, scale, and fleece. The very trunks of the trees she has protected against the effects of heat and cold by a bark, which is, in some cases, twofold. Man alone, at the very moment of his birth cast naked upon the naked earth, does she abandon to cries, to lamentations, and, a thing that is the case with no other animal whatever, to tears: this, too, from the very moment that he enters upon existence. But as for laughter, why, by Hercules!—to laugh, if but for an instant only, has never been granted to man before the fortieth day from his birth, and then it is looked upon as a miracle of precocity. Introduced thus to the light, man has wrappings instantly put upon all his limbs, a thing that falls to the lot of none of the brutes that are born among us. Born to such singular good fortune, there lies the animal, which is destined to command all the others, lies, fast bound hand and foot, and weeping aloud! such being the penalty which he has to pay on beginning life, and that for the sole fault of having been born. Alas! for the folly of those who can think after such a beginning as this, that they have been born for the display of vanity!

The earliest presage of future strength, the earliest

bounty of time, confers upon him nought but the resemblance to a quadruped. How soon does man gain the power of walking? How soon does he gain the faculty of speech? How soon is his mouth fitted for mastication? How long are the pulsations of the crown of his head to proclaim him the weakest of all animated beings? And then, the diseases to which he is subject, the numerous remedies which he is obliged to devise against his maladies, and those thwarted every now and then by new forms and features of disease. While other animals have an instinctive knowledge of their natural powers; some, of their swiftness of pace, some of their rapidity of flight, and some of their power of swimming; man is the only one that knows nothing, that can learn nothing without being taught; he can neither speak nor walk nor eat and, in short, he can do nothing at the prompting of nature but weep. For this it is, that many have been of opinion that it were better not to have been born, or if born, to have been annihilated at the earliest possible moment.

To man alone of all animated beings has it been given to grieve, to be guilty of luxury and excess; and that in modes innumerable and in every part of his body. Man is the only being that is a prey to ambition, to avarice, to an immoderate desire of life, to superstition,—he is the only one that troubles himself about his burial, and even what is to become of him after death. By none is life held on a tenure more frail, none are more influenced by desires for all things; none are sensible of fears more bewildering; none are actuated by rage more frantic and violent. Other animals live at peace with those of their own kind; we only see them unite to make a stand against those of a different species. The fierceness of the lion is not expended in fighting with its own kind; the sting of the serpent is not aimed at the serpent; and the monsters of the sea and the fishes vent their rage only on those of a different species. But with man,—by Hercules! most of *his* misfortunes are occasioned by man.

The Form of the Earth

We always speak of the ball of the earth, and we admit it to be a globe bounded by the poles. It has not indeed the form of an absolute sphere, from the number of lofty mountains and flat plains; but if the termination of the lines be bounded by a curve, this would compose a perfect sphere. And this we learn from arguments drawn from the nature of things, although not from the same considerations which we made use of with respect to the heavens. For in these the hollow convexity everywhere bends on itself, and leans upon the earth as its center. Whereas the earth rises up solid and dense, like something that swells up and is protruded outwards. The heavens bend towards the center, while the earth goes from the center, the continual rolling of the heavens about it forcing its immense globe into the form of a sphere.

On this point there is a great contest between the learned and the vulgar. We maintain that there are men dispersed over every part of the earth, that they stand with their feet turned towards each other, that the vault of the heavens appears alike to all of them, and that all of them appear to tread equally on the middle of the earth. If any one should ask why those situated opposite to us do not fall, we directly ask in return whether those on the opposite side do not wonder that we do not fall. But I may make a remark that will appear plausible even to the most unlearned, that if the earth were of the figure of an unequal globe, like the seed of a pine, still it may be inhabited in every part.

But of how little moment is this when we have another miracle rising up to our notice! The earth itself is pendent and does not fall with us; it is doubtful whether this be from the force of the spirit which is contained in the universe, or whether it would fall, did not nature resist, by allowing of no place where it might fall. For as the seat of fire is nowhere but in fire, nor of water except in water, nor of air except in air, so there is no situation for the earth except in itself, everything else repelling it.

The Dimensions of the Earth

Our part of the Earth, floating as it were in the ocean which surrounds it, stretches out to the greatest extent from east to west; from India to the pillars consecrated to Hercules being a distance of 8568 miles, according to the statement of Artemidorus.

The breadth of the Earth from south to north is commonly supposed to be only about one half of its length, or 4490 miles. On each side, the uninhabitable parts have not been discovered.

Eratosthenes, a man who was peculiarly well skilled in all the more subtle parts of learning, has stated the whole circumference of the Earth to be 31,500 miles.

Finite and Infinite

The world, and whatever that be which we otherwise call the heavens, by the vault of which all things are enclosed, we must conceive to be a Deity, to be eternal, without bounds, neither created, nor subject, at any time, to destruction. To inquire what is beyond it is no concern of man, nor can the human mind form any conjecture respecting it. It is sacred, eternal, and without bounds, including everything in itself; finite, yet like what is infinite; the most certain of all things, yet like what is uncertain, externally and internally embracing all things in itself; it is the work of nature, and itself constitutes nature.

It is madness to harass the mind, as some have done, with attempts to measure the world, and to publish these attempts; or, like others, to argue from what they have made out, that there are innumerable other worlds, and that we must believe there to be so many other natures, or that, if only one nature produced the whole, there will be so many suns and so many moons, and that each of them will have immense trains of other heavenly bodies. The same questions recur at every step of our inquiry, anxious as we must be to arrive at some termination; this infinity, which we ascribe to nature, the former of all things, can be more easily comprehended by one single formation, especially when that is so extensive. It is madness, perfect madness, to go out of this world and search for what is beyond it, as if one who is ignorant of his own dimensions could ascertain the measure of any thing else, or as if the human mind could see what the world itself cannot contain.

The Form of the World

That it has the form of a perfect globe we learn from the name which has been uniformly given to it, as well as from numerous natural arguments. For not only does a figure of this kind sustain itself, also including itself, requiring no adjustments, not sensible of either end or beginning in any of its parts, and is best fitted for that motion, with which it is continually turning round; but still more, because we perceive it, by the evidence of the sight, to be, in every part, convex and central, which could not be the case were it of any other figure.

The rising and the setting of the sun clearly prove, that this globe is carried round in the space of twenty-four hours, in an eternal and never-ceasing circuit, and with incredible swiftness. I am not able to say, whether the sound caused by the whirling about of so great a mass be excessive, and, therefore, far beyond what our ears can perceive, nor, indeed, whether the resounding of so many stars, all carried along at the same time and revolving in their orbits, may not produce a kind of delightful harmony of incredible sweetness.

The Elements and the Planets

'I do not find that any one has doubted that there are four elements. The highest of these is supposed to be fire, and hence proceed the eyes of so many glittering stars. The next is that spirit, which both the Greeks and ourselves call by the same name, air. It is by the force of this vital principle, pervading all things and mingling with all, that the earth, together with the fourth element, water, is balanced in the middle of space. These are mutually bound together, the lighter being restrained by the heavier, so that they cannot fly off; while, on the contrary, from the lighter tending upwards, the heavier are so suspended, that they cannot fall down. Thus, by an equal tendency in an opposite direction, each of them remains in its appropriate place, bound together by the never-ceasing revolution of the world, which always turning on itself, the earth falls to the lowest part and is in the middle of the whole, while it remains suspended in the center, and, as it were, balancing this center, in which it is suspended. So that it alone remains immovable, whilst all things revolve round it, being connected with every other part, whilst they all rest upon it.

Between this body and the heavens there are suspended, in this aërial spirit, seven stars, separated by determinate spaces, which, on account of their motion, we call wandering, although, in reality, none are less so. The sun is carried along in the midst of these, a body of great size and power, the ruler, not only of the seasons and of the different climates, but also of the stars themselves and of the heavens. When we consider his operations, we must regard him as the life, or rather the mind of the universe, the chief regulator and the God of nature; he also lends his light to the other stars. He is most illustrious and excellent, beholding all things and hearing all things, which, I perceive, is ascribed to him exclusively by the prince of poets, Homer.

God

I consider it an indication of human weakness to inquire into the figure and form of God. For whatever God be, if there be any other God, and wherever he exists, he is all sense, all sight, all hearing, all life, all mind, and all within himself. To believe that there are a number of Gods, derived from the virtues and vices of man, as Chastity, Concord, Understanding, Hope, Honor, Clemency, and Fidelity; or, according to the opinion of Democritus, that there are only two, Punishment and Reward, indicates still greater folly. Human nature, weak and frail as it is, mindful of its own infirmity, has made these divisions, so that every one might have recourse to that which he supposed himself to stand more particularly in need of. Hence we find different names employed by different nations; the inferior deities are arranged in classes, and diseases and plagues are deified, in consequence of our anxious wish to propitiate them. It was from this cause that a temple was dedicated to Fever, at the public expense, on the Palatine Hill, and to Orbona, near the Temple of the Lares, and that an altar was elected to Good Fortune on the Esquiline. Hence we may understand how it comes to pass that there is a greater population of the Celestials than of human beings, since each individual makes a separate God for himself, adopting his own Juno and his own Genius. And there are nations who make Gods of certain animals, and even certain obscene things, which are not to be spoken of, swearing by stinking meats and such like. To suppose that marriages are contracted between the Gods, and that, during so long a period, there should have been no issue from them, that some of them should be old and always gray-headed and others young and like children, some of a dark complexion, winged, lame, produced from eggs, living and dying on alternate days, is sufficiently puerile and foolish. But it is the height of impudence to imagine that adultery takes place between them, that they have contests and quarrels, and that there are Gods of theft and of various crimes. To assist man is to be a God; this is the path to eternal glory. This is the path which the Roman nobles formerly pursued, and this is the path which is now pursued by the greatest ruler of our age, Vespasian Augustus, he who has come to the relief of an exhausted empire, as well as by his sons. This was the ancient mode of remunerating those who deserved it, to regard them as Gods. For the names of all the Gods have been derived from their services to mankind. And with respect to Jupiter and Mercury, and the rest of the celestial nomenclature, who does not admit that they have reference to certain natural phenomena?

But it is ridiculous to suppose, that the great head of all things, whatever it be, pays any regard to human affairs. Can we believe, or rather can there be any doubt, that it is not polluted by such a disagreeable and complicated office? It is not easy to determine which opinion would be most for the advantage of mankind, since we observe some who have no respect for the Gods, and others who carry it to a scandalous excess. They are slaves to foreign ceremonies; they carry on their fingers the Gods and the monsters whom they worship; they condemn and they lay great stress on certain kinds of food; they impose on themselves dreadful ordinances, not even sleeping quietly. They do not marry or adopt children, or indeed do anything else, without the sanction of their sacred rites. There are others, on the contrary, who will cheat in the very Capitol, and will forswear themselves even by Jupiter Tonans, and while these thrive in their crimes the others torment themselves with their superstitions to no purpose.

Among these discordant opinions mankind have discovered for themselves a kind of intermediate deity, by which our scepticism concerning God is still increased. For all over the world, in all places, and at all times, Fortune is the only god whom every one invokes; she alone is spoken of, she alone is accused and is supposed to be guilty; she alone is in our thoughts, is praised and blamed, and is loaded with reproaches; wavering as she is, conceived by the generality of mankind to be blind, wandering, inconstant, uncertain, variable, and often favoring the unworthy. To her are referred all our losses and all our gains, and in casting up the accounts of mortals she alone balances the two pages of our sheet. We are so much in the power of chance, that change itself is considered as a God, and the existence of God becomes doubtful.

But there are others who reject this principle and assign events to the influence of the stars, and to the laws of our nativity; they suppose that God, once for all, issues his decrees and never afterwards interferes. This opinion begins to gain ground and both the learned and the unlearned vulgar are falling into it. Hence we have the admonitions of thunder, the warnings of oracles, the predictions of soothsayers, and things too trifling to be mentioned, such as sneezing and stumbling with the feet reckoned among omens. The late Emperor Augustus relates that he put the left shoe on the wrong foot the day when he was near being assaulted by his soldiers. And such things as these so embarrass improvident mortals, that among all of them this alone is certain, that there is nothing certain and that there is nothing more proud or more wretched than man. For other animals have no care but to provide for their subsistence, for which the spontaneous kindness of nature is all-sufficient; and this one circumstance renders their lot more especially preferable, that they never think about glory or money or ambition and, above all, that they never reflect on death.

The belief, however, that on these points the Gods

superintend human affairs is useful to us, as well as that the punishment of crimes, although sometimes tardy, from the Deity being occupied with such a mass of business, is never entirely remitted and that the human race was not made the next in rank to himself, in order that they might be degraded like brutes. And indeed this constitutes the great comfort in this imperfect state of man, that even the Deity cannot do everything. For he cannot procure death for himself, even if he wished it, which, so numerous are the evils of life, has been granted to man as our chief good. Nor can he make mortals immortal, or recall to life those who are dead; nor can he effect that he who has once lived shall not have lived, or that he who has enjoyed honors shall not have enjoyed them; nor has he any influence over past events but to cause them to be forgotten. And, if we illustrate the nature of our connection with God by a less serious argument, he cannot make twice ten not to be twenty, and many other things of this kind. By these considerations the power of Nature is clearly proved and is shown to be what we call God. It is not foreign to the subject to have digressed into these matters, familiar as they are to every one, from the continual discussions that take place respecting God.

The Nature of the Stars

Let us return from this digression to the other parts of nature. The stars which are described as fixed in the heavens are not, as the vulgar suppose, attached each of them to different individuals, the brighter to the rich, those that are less so to the poor, and the dim to the aged, shining according to the lot of the individual, and separately assigned to mortals; for they have neither come into existence, nor do they perish in connection with particular persons, nor does a falling star indicate that any one is dead.

We are not so closely connected with the heavens as that the shining of the stars is affected by our death.

The Manes, or Departed Spirits

After burial come the different quiddities as to the existence of the Manes. All men, after their last day, return to what they were before the first; and after death there is no more sensation left in the body or in the soul than there was before birth. But this same vanity of ours extends even to the future, and lyingly fashions to itself an existence even in the very moments which belong to death itself: at one time it has conferred upon us the immortality of the soul; at another transmigration; and at another it has given sensation to the shades below, and paid divine honors to the departed spirit, thus making a kind of deity of him who has but just ceased to be a man. As if the mode of breathing with man was in any way different from that of other animals, and as if there were not many other animals to be found whose life is longer than that of man, and yet for whom no one ever presaged anything of a like immortality. For what is the actual substance of the soul, when taken by itself? Of what material does it consist? Where is the seat of its thoughts? How is it to see, or hear, or how to touch? And then of what use is it, or what can it avail, if it has not these faculties? Where is its residence, and what vast multitudes of these souls and spirits must there be after the lapse of so many ages? But all these are the mere figments of childish ravings and of that mortality which is so anxious never to cease to exist. It is a similar piece of vanity to preserve the dead bodies of men; just like the promise that he shall come to life again which was made by Democritus who never has come to life again himself. Out upon it! What downright madness is it to suppose that life is to recommence after death! or indeed what repose are we ever to enjoy when we have been once born, if the soul is to retain its consciousness in heaven, and the shades of the dead in the infernal regions? This pleasing delusion and this credulity quite cancel that chief good of human nature, death, and as it were, double the misery of him who is about to die by anxiety as to what is to happen to him after it.

How much more easy and how much more devoid of all doubts is it for each of us to put his trust in himself, and guided by our knowledge of what our state has been before birth, to assume that that after death will be the same.

ODD PEOPLE

Wonders

India, and the region of Ethiopia more especially, abounds in wonders. In India the largest of animals are produced; their dogs, for example, are much bigger than those of any other country. The trees are said to be of such vast height that it is impossible to send an arrow over them. This is the result of the singular fertility of the soil, the equable temperature of the atmosphere, and the abundance of water; which, if we are to believe what is said, are such that a single fig-tree is capable of affording shelter to a whole troop of horse. The reeds here are also of such enormous length that each portion of them, between the joints, forms a tube of which a boat is made that is capable of holding three men. It is a well-known fact that many of the people here are more than five cubits in height. These people never expectorate, are subject to no pains, either in the head, the teeth, or the eyes, and rarely in any other parts of the body; so well is the heat of the sun calculated to strengthen the constitution. Their philosophers, who are called Gymnosophists, remain in one posture with their eyes immovably fixed upon the sun from its rising to its setting, and during the whole of the day they are accustomed to stand in the burning sands on one foot, first one and then the other. According to the account of Megasthenes, dwelling upon a mountain called Nulo there is a race of men who have their feet turned backwards, with eight toes on each foot.

On many of the mountains there is a tribe of men who have the heads of dogs and clothe themselves with the skins of wild beasts. Instead of speaking they bark; and furnished with claws, they live by hunting and catching birds. According to the story, as given by Ctesias, the number of these people is more than a hundred and twenty thousand: and the same author tells us that there is a certain race in India, of which the females are pregnant once only in the course of their lives, and that the hair of the children becomes white the instant they are born. He speaks also of another race of men who are known as Monocoli who have only one leg but are able to leap with surprising agility. The same people are also called Sciapodæ because they are in the habit of lying on their backs during the time of the extreme heat, and protect themselves from the sun by the shade of their feet. These people, he says, dwell not very far from the Troglodytæ; to the west of whom again there is a tribe who are without necks and have eyes in their shoulders.

Marvelous Births

That three children are sometimes produced at one birth is a well-known fact; the case, for instance, of the Horatii and the Curiatii. Where a greater number of children than this is produced at one birth it is looked upon as portentous, except in Egypt, where the water of the river Nile, which is used for drink, is a promoter of fecundity. Very recently, towards the close of the reign of the Emperor Augustus, now deified, a certain woman of the lower orders, at Ostia, whose name was Fausta brought into the world at one birth two male children and two females, a presage, no doubt, of the famine which shortly after took place. We find it stated also that in Peloponnesus a woman was delivered of five children at a birth four successive times, and that the greater part of all these children survived. Trogus informs us that in Egypt as many as seven children are occasionally produced at one birth.

Individuals are occasionally born who belong to both sexes; such persons we call by the name of hermaphrodites.

They were formerly called Androgyni and were looked upon as monsters, but at the present day they are employed for sensual purposes.

Eutychis of Tralles was borne to the funeral pile by twenty of her children, having had thirty in all. Also Alcippe was delivered of an elephant—but then that must be looked upon as a prodigy; as in the case where, at the commencement of the Marsian war, a female slave was delivered of a serpent. Among these monstrous births there are beings produced which unite in one body the forms of several creatures. For instance, Claudius Cæsar informs us in his writings, that a Hippocentaur was born in Thessaly but died on the same day: and indeed I have seen one myself which in the reign of that emperor was brought to him from Egypt, preserved in honey. We have a case also of a child at Saguntum which returned immediately into its mother's womb, the same year in which that place was destroyed by Hannibal.

The change of females into males is undoubtedly no fable. We find it stated in the Annals that in the consulship of P. Licinius Crassus and C. Cassius Longinus a girl who was living at Casinum with her parents was changed into a boy; and that by the command of the Aruspices he was conveyed away to a desert island. Licinius Mucianus informs us that he once saw at Argos a person whose name was then Arescon, though he had been formerly called Arescusa: that this person had been married to a man, but that, shortly after, a beard and marks of virility made their appearance, upon which he took to himself a wife. He had also seen a boy at Smyrna to whom the very same thing had happened. I myself saw in Africa one L. Cossicius, a citizen of Thysdris, who had been changed into a man the very day on which he was married to a husband.

Giants and Dwarfs

It is a well-known fact that at the age of three years the body of each person is half the height that it will ever attain. Taking it all in all, it is observed that in the human race the stature is almost daily becoming less and less, and sons are rarely taller than their parents.

The tallest man that has been seen in our times was Gabbaras who was brought from Arabia by the Emperor Claudius; his height was nine feet and as many inches. In the reign of Augustus there were two persons, Posio and Secundilla, who were half a foot taller than he; their bodies have been preserved as objects of curiosity in the museum of the Sallustian family.

In the reign of the same emperor, there was a man remarkable for his extremely diminutive stature, being only two feet and a palm in height; his name was Conopas, and he was a great pet with Julia, the granddaughter of Augustus. There was a female also of the same size, Andromeda by name, a freed woman of Julia Augusta. We learn from Varro that Manius Maximus and M. Tullius, members of our equestrian order, were only two cubits in height; and I have myself seen them, preserved in their coffins. It is far from an unknown fact that children are occasionally born a foot and a half in height, and sometimes a little more; such children, however, have finished their span of existence by the time they are three years old.

Strong Men

Varro, speaking of persons remarkable for their strength, gives us an account of Tributanus a celebrated gladiator skilled in the use of the Samnite arms; he was a man of meager person, but possessed of extraordinary strength. Varro makes mention of his son also, who served in the army of Pompeius Magnus. He says, that in all parts of his body, even in the arms and hands, there was a network of sinews extending across and across. The latter of these men, having been challenged by an enemy, with a single finger of the right hand, and that unarmed, vanquished him and then seized and dragged him to the camp. Vinnius Valens who served as a centurion in the prætorian guard of Augustus was in the habit of holding up wagons laden with casks until they were emptied; and of stopping a carriage with one hand and holding it back against all the efforts of the horses to drag it forward. He performed other wonderful feats also, an account of which may still be seen inscribed on his monument. Varro also gives the following statement: "Fusius, who used to be called the 'bumpkin Hercules,' was in the habit of carrying his own mule; while Salvius was able to mount a ladder with a weight of two hundred pounds attached to his feet, the same to his hands, and two hundred pounds on each shoulder." I myself once saw—a most marvelous display of strength—a man of the name of Athanatus walk across the stage wearing a leaden breastplate of five hundred pounds weight, while shod with buskins of the same weight. When Milo the wrestler had once taken his stand there was not a person who could move him from his position; and when he grasped an apple in his hand no one could so much as open one of his fingers.

There are men in the Circus who are able to keep on running for a distance of one hundred and sixty miles; and lately, in the consulship of Fonteius and Vipstanus, there was a child eight years of age who, between morning and evening, ran a distance of seventy-five miles. We become all the more sensible of these wonderful instances of swiftness upon reflecting that Tiberius Nero, when he made all possible haste to reach his brother Drusus who was then sick in Germany, reached him in three stages, traveling day and night on the road; the distance of each stage was two hundred miles.

Acuteness of Sight

Instances of acuteness of sight are to be found stated, which exceed all belief. Cicero informs us that the Iliad of Homer was written on a piece of parchment so small as to be enclosed in a nutshell. He makes mention also of a man who could distinguish objects at a distance of one hundred and thirty-five miles. M. Varro says that the name of this man was Strabo, and that, during the Punic war, from Lilybæum the promontory of Sicily, he was in the habit of seeing the fleet come out of the harbor of Carthage, and could even count the number of the vessels.

Vigor of Mind

The most remarkable instance, I think, of vigor of mind in any man ever born was that of Cæsar the Dictator. I am not at present alluding to his valor and courage, nor yet his exalted genius, which was capable of embracing everything under the face of heaven, but I am speaking of that innate vigor of mind which was so peculiar to him, and that promptness which seemed to act like a flash of lightning. We find it stated that he was able to write or read, and at the same time to dictate and listen. He could dictate to his secretaries four letters at once, and those on the most important business; and, if he was busy about nothing else, as many as seven. He fought fifty pitched battles, being the only commander who exceeded M. Marcellus in this respect, he having fought only thirty-nine. In addition to the victories gained by him in the civil wars, one million one hundred and ninety-two thousand men were slain by him in his battles. For my own part, I am not going to set down as a subject for high renown what was really an outrage committed upon mankind, even though he may have been acting under the strong influence of necessity; and indeed he himself confesses as much in his omission to state the number of persons who perished by the sword in the civil wars.

Persons Who Have Come to Life Again

Aviola, a man of consular rank, came to life again when on the funeral pile; but by reason of the violence of the flames no assistance could be rendered him, in consequence of which he was burnt alive. The same thing is said to have happened to L. Lamia, a man of prætorian rank. Messala, Rufus and many other authors inform us that C. Ælius Tubero, who had filled the office of prætor, was also rescued from the funeral pile. Such then is the condition of us mortals: to these and the like vicissitudes of fortune are we born; so much so that we cannot be sure of anything, no, not even that a person is dead. With reference to the soul of man, we find, among other instances, that the soul of Hermotinus of Clazomenæ was in the habit of leaving his body and wandering into distant countries, whence it brought back numerous accounts of various things which could not have been obtained by any one but a person who was present. The body in the meantime was left apparently lifeless. At last his enemies, the Cantharidæ as they were called, burned the body so that the soul on its return was deprived of its sheath, as it were. It is stated also that in Proconnesus the soul of Aristeas was seen to fly out of his mouth under the form of a raven; a most fabulous story which may be well ranked with the one that follows. It is told of Epimenides of Cnossus that when he was a boy, being fatigued by heat and walking, he fell asleep in a cave where he slept for fifty-seven years;

and that when he awoke, as though it had been on the following day, he was much astonished at the changes which he saw in the appearance of every thing around him: after this, old age, it is said, came upon him in an equal number of days with the years he had slept, but his life was prolonged to his hundred and fifty-seventh year.

The Druids of Gaul

Druids—for that is the name they give to their magicians—held nothing more sacred than the mistletoe and the tree that bears it, supposing always that tree to be the robur. Of itself the robur is selected by them to form whole groves, and they perform none of their religious rites without employing branches of it; so much so that it is very probable that the priests themselves may have received their name from the Greek name for that tree. In fact, it is the notion with them that everything that grows on it has been sent immediately from heaven, and that the mistletoe upon it is a proof that the tree has been selected by God himself as an object of his especial favor.

The mistletoe is rarely found upon the robur; and when found is gathered with rites replete with religious awe. This is done more particularly on the fifth day of the moon, the day which is the beginning of their months and years, as also of their ages, which are but thirty years. This day they select because the moon, though not yet in the middle of her course, has already considerable power and influence; and they call her by a name which signifies, in their language, the all-healing. Having made all due preparation for the sacrifice and a banquet beneath the trees, they bring thither two white bulls, the horns of which are bound then for the first time. Clad in a white robe the priest ascends the tree, and cuts the mistletoe with a golden sickle, which is received by others in a white cloak. They then immolate the victims, offering up their prayers that

God will render this gift of his propitious to those to whom he has so granted it. It is the belief with them that the mistletoe, taken in drink, will impart fecundity to all animals that are barren, and that it is an antidote for all poisons. Such are the religious feelings which we find entertained towards trifling objects among nearly all nations.

The Essenes

The Essenes are a people that live apart from the world, and marvelous beyond all others throughout the whole earth, for they have no women among them; to sexual desire they are strangers; money they have none; the palm trees are their only companions. Day after day, however, their numbers are fully recruited by multitudes of strangers that resort to them, driven thither to adopt their usages by the tempests of fortune, and wearied with the miseries of life. Thus it is that through thousands of ages, incredible to relate, this people eternally prolongs its existence without a single birth taking place there; so fruitful a source of population to it is that weariness of life which is felt by others. Below this people was formerly the town of Engadda, second only to Hierosolyma in the fertility of its soil and its groves of palm trees; now, like it, another heap of ashes.

THE CHEF

Goose Liver

Our people only esteem the goose for the goodness of its liver. When they are crammed this grows to a very large size, and on being taken from the animal is made still larger by being soaked in honeyed milk. It is matter of debate who it was that first discovered so great a delicacy; whether Scipio Metellus, a man of consular dignity, or M. Seius, a contemporary of his and a Roman of equestrian rank. However, a thing about which there is no dispute, it was Messalinus Cotta the son of the orator Messala who first discovered the art of roasting the webbed feet of the goose and of cooking them in a ragout with cocks' combs: for I shall faithfully award each culinary palm to such as I shall find deserving of it. It is a wonderful fact in relation to this bird that it comes on foot all the way from the country of the Morini to Rome; those that are tired are placed in the front rank, while the rest, taught by a natural instinct to move in a compact body, drive them on.

M. Appicus made the discovery that we may employ the same artificial method of increasing the size of the liver of sows; it consists of cramming them with dried figs, and when they are fat enough they are drenched with wine mixed with honey, and immediately killed.

Oysters

Oysters love fresh water and spots where numerous rivers discharge themselves into the sea. Still, we do find them breeding among rocks and in places far remote from the contact of fresh water, as in the neighborhood of Grynium and of Myrina, for example. Generally speaking they increase in size with the increase of the moon, but it is at the beginning of summer, more particularly and when the rays of the sun penetrate the shallow waters, that they are swollen with an abundance of milk. This would appear to be the reason why they are so small when found out at sea; the opacity of the water tending to arrest their growth, and the moping consequent thereon producing a comparative indisposition for food.

Oysters are of various colors; in Spain they are red, in Illyricum of a tawny hue, and at Circeii black, both in meat and shell. But in every country those oysters are the most highly esteemed that are compact without being slimy from their secretions, and are remarkable more for their thickness than their breadth. They should never be taken in either muddy or sandy spots, but from a firm, hard bottom; the meat should be compressed and not of a fleshy consistence; and the oyster should be free from fringed edges and lying wholly in the cavity of the shell. Persons of experience in these matters add another characteristic; a fine purple thread, they say, should run round the margins of the beard, this being looked upon as a sign of superior quality.

The first person who formed artificial oyster beds was Sergius Orata who established them at Baiæ in the time of L. Crassus, the orator, just before the Marsic War. This was done by him not for the gratification of gluttony, but of avarice, as he contrived to make a large income by this exercise of his ingenuity. He was the first, too, to invent hanging baths, and after buying villas and trimming them up he would every now and then sell them again. He was the first to adjudge the preëminence for delicacy of flavor to the oysters of Lake Lucrinus; for every kind of aquatic animal is superior in one place to what it is in another. Thus, for instance, the wolf-fish of the river Tiber is the best that is caught between the two bridges, and the turbot of Ravenna is the most esteemed, the murena of Sicily, the elops of Rhodes; the same, too, as to the other kinds, not to go through all the items of the culinary catalogue. The British shores had not as yet sent their supplies at the time when Orata thus ennobled the Lucrine oysters: at a later period it was thought worth while to fetch oysters all the way from Brundisium at the very extremity of Italy; and in order that there might exist no rivalry between the two flavors a plan has been more recently hit upon, of feeding the oysters of Brundisium in Lake Lucrinus, famished as they must naturally be after so long a journey.

Other Fish

In the same age, Licinius Murena was the first to form preserves for other fish, and his example was soon followed by the noble families of the Philippi and the Hortensii. Lucullus had a mountain pierced near Naples, at a greater outlay even than that which had been expended on his villa; and here he formed a channel and admitted the sea to his preserves; it was for this reason that Pompeius Magnus gave him the name of "Xerxes in a toga." After his death, the fish in his preserves were sold for the sum of four million sesterces.

C. Hirrus was the first person who formed preserves for the murena; and it was he who lent six thousand of these fishes for the triumphal banquets of Cæsar the Dictator; on which occasion he had them duly weighed, as he declined to receive the value of them in money or any other commodity. His villa, which was of a very humble character in the interior, sold for four million sesterces, in consequence of the valuable nature of the stock ponds there. Next after this there arose a passion for individual fish. At Bauli in the territory of Baiæ the orator Hortensius had some fish preserves in which there was a murena to which he became so much attached as to be supposed to have wept on hearing of its death. It was at the same villa that Antonia, the wife of Drusus, placed earrings upon a murena which she had become fond of; the report of which singular circumstance attracted many visitors to the place.

Fulvius Lupinus first formed preserves for sea snails, in the territory of Tarquinii, shortly before the civil war between Cæsar and Pompeius Magnus. He also carefully distinguished them by their several species, separating them from one another. The white ones were those that are produced in the district of Reate, those of Illyria were remarkable for the largeness of their size; while those from Africa were the most prolific; those, however, from the Promontory of the Sun were the most esteemed of all. For the purpose of fattening them he invented a mixture of boiled wine, spelt meal, and other substances; so that fattened periwinkles even became quite an object of gastronomy; and the art of breeding them was brought to such a pitch of perfection that the shell of a single animal would hold as much as eighty quadrantes (15 quarts).

At the later period they set the highest value on the lupus (bass) and the asellus, as we learn from Cornelius Nepos and the poet Laberius, the author of the Mimes. The most approved kinds of the lupus are those which have the name of "lanati," or "woolly," in consequence of the extreme whiteness and softness of the flesh. Of the asellus there are two sorts, the callarias which is the smallest, and the bacchus which is only taken in deep water, and is hence much preferred to the former. On the other hand, among the varieties of the lupus those are the most esteemed which are taken in rivers.

At the present day, the first place is given to the scarus, the only fish that is said to ruminate, and to feed on grass and not on other fish. It is mostly found in the Carpathian Sea and never of its own accord passes Lectum, a promontory of Troas. Optatus Elipertius, the commander of the fleet under the Emperor Claudius, had this fish brought from that locality and dispersed in various places off the coast between Ostia and the districts of Campania.

During five years the greatest care was taken that those which were caught should be returned to the sea; but since then they have been always found in great abundance off the shores of Italy where formerly there were none to be taken. Thus has gluttony introduced these fish to be a dainty within its reach, and added a new inhabitant to the seas; so that we ought to feel no surprise that foreign birds breed at Rome.

The fish that is next in estimation for the table is the mustela, but that is valued only for its liver. A singular thing to tell of—the lake of Brigantia in Rhætia, lying in the midst of the Alps, produces them to rival even those of the sea.

Of the remaining fish that are held in any degree of esteem, the mullet is the most highly valued as well as the most abundant of all; it is of only a moderate size, rarely exceeds two pounds in weight, and will never grow beyond that weight in preserves or fish ponds. These fish only in the Northern Ocean exceed two pounds in weight, and even there in none but the more westerly parts. Fenestella is of opinion that this fish received its name of mullet [mullus] from its resemblance to the color of the red or mullet-colored shoes. The mullet spawns three times a year: at all events the fry makes its appearance that number of times. The masters in gastronomy inform us that the mullet, while dying, assumes a variety of colors and a succession of shades and that the hue of the red scales, growing paler and paler, gradually changes, more especially if it is looked at enclosed in glass. M. Apicius, a man who displayed a remarkable degree of ingenuity in everything relating to luxury, was of opinion that it was a most excellent plan to let the mullet die in the pickle known as the "garum of the allies"—for we find that even this has found a surname—and he proposed a prize for any one who should invent a new sauce made from the liver of this fish. I find it much easier to relate this fact, than to state who it was that gained the prize.

Asinius Celer, a man of consular rank, and remarkable
for his prodigal expenditure on this fish, bought one at
Rome, during the reign of Caius, at the price of eight thousand sesterces.

Licinius Mucianus relates that in the Red Sea there was
caught a mullet eighty pounds in weight. What a price
would have been paid for it by our epicures, if it had only
been found off the shores in the vicinity of our city!

Wild Boar

The flesh of the wild boar is esteemed. Cato the Censor, in his orations, strongly declaimed against the use of
the brawn of the wild boar. The animal used to be divided
into three portions, the middle part of which was laid by
and called boar's chine. P. Servilius Rullus was the first
Roman who served up a whole boar at a banquet; the father
of that Rullus, who, in the consulship of Cicero, proposed
the Agrarian law. So recent is the introduction of a thing
which is now in daily use. The Annalists have taken
notice of such a fact as this, clearly as a hint to us to
mend our manners, seeing that nowadays two or three
boars are consumed, not at one entertainment, but as forming the first course only.

Fulvius Lupinus was the first Roman who formed
parks for the reception of these and other wild animals.

Fowls

The people of Delos were the first to cram poultry;
and it is with them that originated that abominable mania
for devouring fattened birds larded with the grease of their
own bodies. I find in the ancient sumptuary regulations as
to banquets that this was forbidden for the first time by a
law of the consul Caius Fannius, eleven years before the

Third Punic War; by which it was ordered that no bird should be served at table beyond a single pullet, and that not fattened; an article which has since made its appearance in all the sumptuary laws. A method has been devised of evading it by feeding poultry upon food that has been soaked in milk: prepared in this fashion they are considered even still more delicate. All pullets, however, are not looked upon as equally good for the purposes of fattening, and only those are selected which have a fatty skin about the neck. Then come all the arts of the kitchen—that the thighs may have a nice plump appearance, that the bird may be properly divided down the back, and that poultry may be brought to such a size that a single leg shall fill a whole platter.

Parrot Pie

The first person who invented aviaries for the reception of all kinds of birds was M. Lænius Strabo, a member of the equestrian order, who resided at Brundisium. It was in his time that we thus began to imprison animals to which Nature had assigned the heavens as their element.

But more remarkable than anything in this respect is the story of the dish of Clodius Æsopus, the tragic actor, which was valued at one hundred thousand sesterces, and in which were served up nothing but birds that had been remarkable for their song or their imitation of the human voice, and purchased, each of them, at the price of six thousand sesterces; he being induced to this folly by no other pleasure than that in these he might eat the closest imitators of man; never for a moment reflecting that his own immense fortune had been acquired by the advantages of his voice.

Mushrooms

The safest fungi are those the flesh of which is red.
The next best are the white ones, the stems of which have
a head very similar to the apex worn by the Flamens; and
a third kind are the suilli, very conveniently adapted for
poisoning. Indeed, it is but very recently that they have
carried off whole families, and all the guests at a banquet;
Annæus Serenus, for instance, the prefect of Nero's guard,
together with all the tribunes and centurions. What great
pleasure can there be in partaking of a dish of so doubtful
a character as this? Some persons have classified fungi according to the trees to which they are indebted for their
formation, the fig, for instance, the fennel giant, and the
gummiferous trees; those belonging to the beech, the robur,
and the cypress, not being edible. But who is there to give
us a guarantee when they come to market, that these distinctions have been observed?

I would here also give some general directions for the
cooking of mushrooms, as this is the only article of food
that the voluptuaries of the present day are in the habit of
dressing with their own hands, and so feeding upon it in
anticipation, being provided with amber-handled knives
and silver plates and dishes for the purpose. Those fungi
may be looked upon as bad which become hard in cooking;
while those are comparatively innoxious which admit
of being thoroughly boiled with the addition of some niter.
They will be all the safer if they are boiled with meat or
the stalks of pears: it is a very good plan, too, to eat pears
directly after them. Vinegar, being of a nature diametri-
cally opposed to them, neutralizes their dangerous qualities.

Olives

Olives from the parts beyond sea are preferred for table to those of Italy, though they are very inferior to them for making oil.

In Italy, those of Pecenum and of Sidicina are considered the best for table. These are kept apart from the others and steeped in salt, after which, like other olives, they are put in amurca, or else boiled wine; some of them are left to float solely in their own oil without any adventitious mode of preparation, and are then known as colymbades: sometimes the berry is crushed and then seasoned with green herbs to flavor it. Even in an unripe state the olive is rendered fit for eating by being sprinkled with boiling water; it is quite surprising how readily it will imbibe sweet juices, and retain an adventitious flavor from foreign substances. With this fruit, as with the grape, there are purple varieties, and the posia is of a complexion approaching to black. Besides those already mentioned there are the superba and a remarkably luscious kind which dries of itself and is even sweeter than the raisin: this last variety is extremely rare and is to be found in Africa and in the vicinity of Emerita in Lusitania.

The oil of the olive is prevented from getting thick and rancid by the admixture of salt. By making an incision in the bark of the tree an aromatic odor may be imparted to the oil. Any other mode of seasoning, such as those used with reference to wine, is not at all gratifying to the palate; nor do we find so many varieties in oil as there are in the produce of the grape, there being in general but three different degrees of goodness. In fine oil the odor is more penetrating, but even in the very best it is but shortlived.

It is one of the properties of oil to impart warmth to the body and to protect against the action of cold; while at the same time it promotes coolness in the head when heated. The Greeks, those parents of all vices, have abused it by making it minister to luxury and employing it commonly in the gymnasium: indeed, it is a well-known fact that the governors of those establishments have sold the scrapings of the oil used there for a sum of eighty thousand sesterces. The majesty of the Roman sway has conferred high honor upon the olive: crowned with it, the troops of the Equestrian order are wont to defile upon the ides of July; it is used, too, by the victor in the minor triumphs of the ovation.

Milk

The most nutritive milk is woman's milk, and next to that goats' milk, to which is owing, probably, the fabulous story that Jupiter was suckled by a goat. The sweetest, next to woman's milk, is camels' milk; but the most efficacious, medicinally speaking, is asses' milk. It is in animals of the largest size and individuals of the greatest bulk, that the milk is secreted with the greatest facility. Goats' milk agrees the best with the stomach, that animal browsing more than grazing. Cows' milk is considered more medicinal, while ewes' milk is sweeter and more nutritive, but not so well adapted to the stomach, it being more oleaginous than any other.

Every kind of milk is more aqueous in spring than in summer, and the same in all cases where the animal has grazed upon a new pasture. The best milk is that which adheres to the fingernail when placed there, and does not run from off it. Milk is most harmless when boiled, more particularly if sea pebbles have been boiled with it. Cows' milk is the most relaxing, and all kinds of milk are less apt to inflate when boiled. Milk is used for all kinds of internal ulcerations, those of the kidneys, bladder, intestines, throat, and lungs in particular; and externally it is employed for itching sensations upon the skin, and for purulent eruptions, it being taken fasting for the purpose. In Arcadia, cows' milk is administered for phthisis, consumption, and cachexy. Instances are cited of persons who have been cured of gout in the hands and feet, by drinking asses' milk.

Mint has the effect of preventing milk from turning sour, or curdling and thickening: hence it is generally put into milk used for drinking.

From milk butter is produced; held as the most delicate of food among barbarous nations, and one which distinguishes the wealthy from the multitude at large. It is mostly made from cows' milk, and hence its name; but the richest butter is that made from ewes' milk. There is a butter made also from goats' milk; but previously to making it, the milk should first be warmed, in winter. In summer it is extracted from the milk by merely shaking it to and fro in a tall vessel with a small orifice at the mouth to admit the air, but otherwise closely stopped, a little water being added to make it curdle the sooner. The milk that curdles the most floats upon the surface; this they remove and, adding salt to it, give it the name of "oxygala." They then take the remaining part and boil it down in pots, and that portion of it which floats on the surface is butter, a substance of an oily nature. The more rank it is in smell, the more highly it is esteemed. When old, it forms an ingredient in numerous compositions. It is of an astringent, emollient, repletive and purgative nature.

Butter has certain of the properties of oil; it is used for an ointment among all barbarian nations, and amongst ourselves for infants.

Cheese

The kinds of cheese that are most esteemed at Rome where the various good things of all nations are to be judged of by comparison, are those which come from the provinces of Nemausus, and more especially the village there of Lesura and Gabalis; but its excellence is only very shortlived and it must be eaten while it is fresh. The pastures of the Alps recommend themselves by two sorts of cheese; the Dalmatic Alps send us the Docleatian cheese, and the Centronian Alps the Vatusican. The kinds produced in the Apennines are more numerous; from Liguria we have the cheese of Ceba which is mostly made from the milk of sheep; from Umbria we have that of Æsina, and from the frontiers of Etruria and Luguria those of Luna, remarkable for their vast size, a single cheese weighing as much as a thousand pounds. Nearer the City we have the cheese of Vestinum, the best of this kind being that which comes from the territory of Ceditium. Goats also produce a cheese which has been of late held in the highest esteem, its flavor being heightened by smoking it. The cheese of this kind which is made at Rome is considered preferable to any other; for that which is made in Gaul has a strong taste like that of medicine. Of the cheese made beyond the sea, that of Bithynia is usually considered the first in quality. That salt exists in pasturelands is pretty evident from the fact that all cheese as it grows old contracts a saltish flavor, even where it does not appear to any great extent; while at the same time it is equally well known that cheese soaked in a mixture of thyme and vinegar will regain its original fresh flavor. It is said that Zoroaster lived thirty years in the wilderness upon cheese, prepared in such a peculiar manner that he was insensible to the advances of old age.

Ice Water

It was the Emperor Nero's invention to boil water and then enclose it in glass vessels and cool it in snow. Indeed it is generally admitted that all water is more wholesome when boiled.

Section IV
WINE LIST

Ancient Wines

The Pramnian wine which Homer has eulogized still retains its ancient fame: it is grown in the territory of Smyrna in the vicinity of the shrine of the Mother of the Gods.

Among the other wines now known we do not find any that enjoyed a high reputation in ancient times. In the year of the consulship of L. Opimius when C. Gracchus, the tribune of the people, engaging in sedition was slain, the growth of every wine was of the very highest quality. In that year the weather was remarkable for its sereneness, and the ripening of the grape, the "coctura," as they call it, was fully effected by the heat of the sun. This was in the year of the City 633. There are wines still preserved of that year's growth, nearly two hundred years ago; they have assumed the consistency of honey, with a rough taste; for such is the nature of wines that, when extremely old, it is impossible to drink them in a pure state; and they require to be mixed with water, as long keeping renders them intolerably bitter. A very small quantity of the Opimian wine, mixed with them, will suffice for the seasoning of other wines. There is no one thing, the value of which increases more than wine does for twenty years, or which decreases with greater rapidity after that period, supposing that the value of it is not by that time greatly enhanced.

Generous Wines

Who can entertain a doubt that some kinds of wine are more agreeable to the palate than others, or that even out of the very same vat there are occasionally produced wines that are by no means of equal goodness, the one being much superior to the other, whether it is that it is owing to the cask, or to some other fortuitous circumstance? Let each person, therefore, constitute himself his own judge as to which kind it is that occupies the preëminence. Livia Augusta who lived to her eighty-second year attributed her longevity to the wine of Pucinum, as she never drank any other. This wine is grown near a bay of the Adriatic, not far from Mount Timavus, upon a piece of elevated rocky ground where the sea-breeze ripens a few grapes, the produce of which supplies a few amphoræ: there is not a wine that is deemed superior to this for medicinal purposes. I am strongly of opinion that this is the same wine, upon which the Greeks have bestowed such wonderful encomiums, under the name of Prætetianum.

The late Emperor Augustus preferred the Setinum to all others, and nearly all the emperors that have succeeded him have followed his example, having learnt from actual experience that there is no danger of indigestion and flatulence resulting from the use of this liquor: this wine is grown in the country that lies just above Forum Appii. In former times the Cæcubum enjoyed the reputation of being the most generous of all the wines; it was grown in some marshy swamps planted with poplars in the vicinity of the Gulf of Amyclæ. This vineyard has now disappeared, the result of the carelessness of the cultivator, combined with its own limited extent and the works on the canal which Nero commenced in order to provide a navigation from Lake Avernus to Ostia.

The second rank belonged to the wine of the Falernian territory, of which the Faustianum was the most choice variety; the result of the care and skill employed upon its cultivation. This, however, has also degenerated very considerably in consequence of the growers being more solicitous about quantity than quality. The Falernian vineyards begin at the bridge of Campania, on the left-hand as you journey towards the Urbana Colonia of Sylla, which was lately a township of the city of Capua. As to the Faustian vineyards, they extend about four miles from a village near Cædiciæ, the same village being six miles from Sinuessa. There is now no wine known that ranks higher than the Falernian; it is the only one among all the wines that takes fire on the application of flame. There are three varieties of it—the rough, the sweet, and the thin. Some persons make the following distinctions: the Caucinum, they say, grows on the summit of this range of hills, the Faustianum on the middle slopes, and the Falernum at the foot: the fact, too, should not be omitted that none of the grapes that produce these more famous wines have by any means an agreeable flavor.

Hydromeli

There is a wine made solely of honey and water. For this purpose it is recommended that rain-water should be kept for a period of five years. Those who show greater skill content themselves with taking the water just after it has fallen and boiling it down to one third, to which they then add one third in quantity of old honey, and keep the mixture exposed to the rays of a hot sun for forty days after the rising of the Dogstar; others rack it off in the course of ten days, and tightly cork the vessels in which it is kept. This beverage is known as "hydromeli," and with age acquires the flavor of wine. It is nowhere more highly esteemed than in Phrygia.

Beer

The people of the Western world have also their intoxicating drinks, made from corn steeped in water. These beverages are prepared in different ways throughout Gaul and the provinces of Spain; under different names, too, though in their results they are the same. The Spanish provinces have even taught us the fact that these liquors are capable of being kept till they have attained a considerable age. Egypt has invented for its use a very similar beverage made from corn; indeed, in no part of the world is drunkenness ever at a loss. And then, besides, they take these drinks unmixed, and do not dilute them with water, the way that wine is modified; and yet, by Hercules! one really might have supposed that there the earth produced nothing but corn for the people's use. Alas! what wondrous skill, and yet how misplaced! Means have been discovered for getting drunk even upon water.

Wine Vessels

The following are among the rules given for the proper management of wines: One side of the wine cellar, or at all events the windows, ought to face northeast, or due east. All dunghills and roots of trees and everything of a repulsive smell ought to be kept at as great a distance as possible, wine being very apt to contract an odor. Fig trees too, either wild or cultivated, ought not to be planted in the vicinity. Intervals should be left between the vessels, in order to prevent infection in case of any of them turning bad, wine being remarkably apt to become tainted. The shape of the vessels is of considerable importance: those that are broad and bellying are not so good. We find it recommended to pitch them immediately after the rising of the Dogstar, and then to wash them either with sea or salt water after which they should be sprinkled with the ashes of tree shoots or else with potters' earth; they ought then to be cleaned out and perfumed with myrrh, a thing which ought to be frequently done to the wine cellars as well. Weak, thin wines should be kept in dolia sunk in the ground, while those in which the stronger ones are kept should be more exposed to the air. The vessels ought on no account to be entirely filled, room being left for seasoning by mixing either raisin wine or else defrutum flavored with saffron; old pitch and sapa are sometimes used for the same purpose. The lids of the dolia ought to be seasoned in a similar manner, with the addition of mastich and Bruttian pitch.

It is strongly recommended never to open the vessels except in fine weather; nor yet while a south wind is blowing, or at a full moon.

The flower of wine when white is looked upon as a good sign; but when it is red it is bad, unless that should happen to be the color of the wine. The vessels should not be hot to the touch, nor should the covers throw out a sort of sweat. When wine very soon flowers on the surface and emits an odor it is a sign that it will not keep.

As to defrutum and sapa, it is recommended to commence boiling them when there is no moon to be seen, or at the conjunction of that planet, and at no other time. Leaden vessels should be used for this purpose, and not copper ones, and walnuts are generally thrown into them from a notion that they absorb the smoke. In Campania they expose the very finest wines in casks in the open air, it being the opinion that it tends to improve the wine if it is exposed to the action of the sun and moon, the rain and the winds.

Drunkenness

If any one will take the trouble duly to consider the matter, he will find that upon no one subject is the industry of man kept more constantly on the alert than upon the making of wine; as if Nature had not given us water as a beverage, the one of which all other animals make use. We, on the other hand, even go so far as to make our very beasts of burden drink wine: so vast are our efforts, so vast our labors, and so boundless the cost which we thus lavish upon a liquid which deprives man of his reason and drives him to frenzy and to the commission of a thousand crimes! So great, however, are its attractions, that a great part of mankind are of opinion that there is nothing else in life worth living for. Nay, what is even more than this, that we may be enabled to swallow all the more, we have adopted the plan of diminishing its strength by pressing it through filters of cloth, and have devised numerous inventions whereby to create an artificial thirst. To promote drinking, we find that even poisonous mixtures have been invented, and some men are known to take a dose of hemlock before they begin to drink, that they may have the fear of death before them to make them take their wine: others take powdered pumice for the same purpose, and various other mixtures which I should feel quite ashamed any further to enlarge upon.

We see the more prudent among those who are given to this habit have themselves parboiled in hot baths, from whence they are carried away half dead. Others there are who cannot wait till they have got to the banqueting couch, no, not so much as till they have got their shirt on, but all naked and panting as they are, the instant they leave the bath they seize hold of large vessels filled with wine, to show off, as it were, their mighty powers, and so gulp down the whole of the contents only to vomit them up again the very next moment. This they will repeat a second and even a third time, just as though they had only been begotten for the purpose of wasting wine, and as if that liquor could not be thrown away without having first passed through the human body. It is to encourage habits such as these that we have introduced the athletic exercises of other countries, such as rolling in the mud, and throwing the arms back to show off a brawny neck and chest. Of all these exercises, thirst, it is said, is the chief and primary object.

And then what vessels are employed for holding wine! carved all over with the representations of adulterous intrigues, as if drunkenness itself was not sufficiently capable of teaching us lessons of lustfulness. Thus we see wines quaffed out of impurities, and inebriety invited even by the hope of a reward—invited, did I say?—may the gods forgive me for saying so, purchased outright. We find one person induced to drink upon the condition that he shall have as much to eat as he has previously drunk, while another has to quaff as many cups as he has thrown points on the dice. Then it is that the roving insatiate eyes are setting a price upon the matron's chastity; and yet, heavy as they are with wine, they do not fail to betray their designs to her husband. Then it is that all the secrets of the mind are revealed; one man is heard to disclose the provisions of his will, another lets fall some expression of fatal import, and so fails to keep to himself words which will be sure to come home to him with a cut throat. And how many a man has met his death in this fashion! Indeed, it has become quite a common proverb that "in wine there is truth."

Should he fortunately escape all these dangers, the drunkard never beholds the rising sun, by which his life of drinking is made all the shorter. From wine, too, comes that pallid hue, those drooping eyelids, those sore eyes, those tremulous hands, unable to hold with steadiness the overflowing vessel, condign punishment in the shape of sleep agitated by Furies during the restless night, and the supreme reward of inebriety, those dreams of monstrous lustfulness and of forbidden delights. Then on the next day there is the breath reeking of the wine cask, and a nearly total obliviousness of everything, from the annihilation of the powers of the memory. And this is what they call "seizing the moments of life!" In reality, while other men lose the day that has gone before, the drinker has already lost the one that is to come.

At Rome it was not lawful for women to drink wine. Among the various anecdotes connected with this subject we find that the wife of Egnatius Mecenius was slain by her husband with a stick because she had drunk some wine from the vat, and that he was absolved from the murder by

Romulus. Fabius Pictor in his Book of Annals has stated that a certain lady, for having opened a purse in which the keys of the wine cellar were kept, was starved to death by her family: and Cato tells us that it was the usage for the male relatives to give the females a kiss in order to ascertain whether they smelt of "temetum"; for it was by that name that wine was then known, whence our word "temulentia," signifying drunkenness. Cn. Domitius, the judge, once gave it as his opinion that a certain woman appeared to him to have drunk more wine than was requisite for her health and without the knowledge of her husband, for which reason he condemned her to lose her dower.

Section V

THE WARDROBE

Different Kinds of Wool

The most esteemed wool of all is that of Apulia, and that which in Italy is called Grecian wool, in other countries Italian. The fleeces of Miletus hold the third rank. The Apulian wool is shorter in the hair and only owes its high character to the cloaks that are made of it. That which comes from the vicinity of Tarentum and Canusium is the most celebrated; and there is a wool from Laodicea in Asia of a similar quality. There is no white wool superior to that of the countries bordering on the Padus. The sheep are not shorn in all countries; in some places it is still the custom to pull off the wool. There are various colors of wool; so much so that we want terms to express them all. Several kinds which are called native are found in Spain; Pollentia in the vicinity of the Alps produces black fleeces of the best quality, Asia, as well as Bætica, the red fleeces, which are called Erythræan; those of Canusium are of a tawny color; and those of Tarentum have their peculiar dark tint. All kinds of wool, when not freed from the grease, possess certain medicinal properties. The wool of Istria is much more like hair than wool and is not suitable for the fabrication of stuffs that have a long nap; so too is that which Salacia in Lusitania finds the most useful for making its checkered cloths. There is a similar wool found about Piscenæ in the province of Narbonensis, as also in Egypt; a garment, when it has been worn for some time, is often embroidered with this wool, and will last for a considerable time.

The thick, flocky wool has been esteemed for the manufacture of carpets from the very earliest times; it is quite clear from what we read in Homer that they were in use in his time. The Gauls embroider them in a different manner from that which is practiced by the Parthians. Wool is compressed also for making a felt which, if soaked in vinegar, is capable of resisting iron; and what is still more will even resist fire, the refuse, when taken out of the vat of the scourer, is used for making mattresses, an invention, I fancy, of the Gauls. At all events, it is by Gallic names that we distinguish the different sort of mattresses at the present day; but I am not able to say at what period wool began to be employed for this purpose. Our ancestors made use of straw for the purpose of sleeping upon, just as they do at present when in camp.

Different Kinds of Cloths

Varro informs us, he himself having been an eye-witness, that in the temple of Sancus the wool was still preserved on the distaff and spindle of Tanaquil who was also called Caia Cæcilia; and he says that the royal waved toga, formerly worn by Servius Tullius and now in the temple of Fortune was made by her. Hence was derived the custom, on the marriage of a young woman, of carrying in the procession a dressed distaff and a spindle with the thread arranged upon it. Tanaquil was the first who wove the straight tunic such as our young people wear with the white toga; newly married women also. Waved garments were at first the most esteemed of all: after which those composed of various colors came into vogue. Fenestella informs us, that togas with a smooth surface, as well as the Phrygian togas, began to be used in the latter part of the reign of Augustus. Thick stuffs, in the preparation of which the poppy was used, are of more ancient date, being mentioned by the poet Lucilius in his lines on Torquatus. The prætexta had its origin among the Etrurians. I find that the trabea was first worn by the kings; embroidered garments are mentioned by Homer, and in this class originated the triumphal robes. The Phrygians first used the needle for this purpose, and hence this kind of garment obtained the name of Phrygionian. King Attalus who also lived in Asia invented the art of embroidering with gold, from which these garments have been called Attalic. Babylon was very famous for making embroidery in different colors, and hence stuffs of this kind have obtained the name of Babylonian. The method of weaving cloth with more than two threads was invented at Alexandria; these cloths are called polymita; it was in Gaul that they were first divided into checkers. Metellus Scipio, in the accusation which he brought against Cato, stated that even in his time Babylonian covers for couches were selling for eight hundred thousand sesterces, and these in the time of the Emperor Nero had risen to four millions. The prætextæ of Servius Tullius with which the statue of Fortune, dedicated by him, was covered, lasted until the death of Sejanus; and it is a remarkable fact that, during a period of five hundred and sixty years they had never become tattered or received injury from moths. I myself have seen the fleece upon the living animals dyed purple, scarlet, and violet—a pound and a half of dye being used for each—just as though they had been produced by Nature in this form to meet the demands of luxury.

Linen and Cotton

The linens of Faventia are preferred for whiteness to those of Alia, which are always unbleached: those of Retovium are remarkable for their extreme fineness combined with substance, and are quite equal in whiteness to the linens of Faventia; but they have none of that fine downy nap upon them which is so highly esteemed by some persons, though equally disliked by others. A thread is made from their flax of considerable strength, smoother and more even, almost, than the spider's web; when tested with the teeth it emits a sharp, clear twang; hence it is that it sells at double the price of the other kinds.

But it is the province of Nearer Spain that produces a linen of the greatest luster, an advantage which it owes to the waters of a stream which washes the city of Tarraco there. The fineness of this linen is quite marvelous, and here it is that the first manufactories of cambric were established. From the same province of Spain, the flax of Zoëla has of late years been introduced into Italy and has been found extremely serviceable for the manufacture of hunting nets. Zoëla is a city of Callæcia, in the vicinity of the Ocean. The flax of Cumæ, in Campania, has its own peculiar merits in the manufacture of nets for fishing and fowling; it is employed also for making hunting nets. For it is from flax that we prepare various textures destined to be no less insidious to the brute creation than they are to ourselves. It is with toils made from the flax of Cumæ that wild boars are taken, the meshes being proof against their bristles: before now, too, we have seen some of these toils of a fineness so remarkable as to allow of being passed through a man's ring, running ropes and all; a single individual being able to carry an amount of nets sufficient to environ a whole forest—a thing which we know to have been done not long ago by Julius Lupus who died prefect of Egypt. This, however, is nothing very surprising, but it really is wonderful that each of the cords was composed of no less than one hundred and fifty threads. Those, no doubt, will be astonished at this, who are not aware that there is preserved in the Temple of Minerva at Lindus in the Isle of Rhodes the cuirass of a former king of Egypt, Amasis by name, each thread employed in the texture of which is composed of three hundred and sixty-five other threads. Mucianus, who was three times consul, informs us that he saw this curiosity very recently, though there was but little then remaining of it in consequence of the injury it had experienced at the hands of various persons who had tried to verify the fact. Italy, too, holds the flax of the

Peligni in high esteem, though it is only employed by fullers; there is no kind known that is whiter than this or which bears a closer resemblance to wool. That grown by the Cadurci is held in high estimation for making mattresses, which are an invention for which we are indebted to the Gauls: the ancient usage of Italy is still kept in remembrance in the word "stramentum," the name given by us to beds stuffed with straw.

The flax of Egypt, though the least strong of all as a tissue, is that from which the greatest profits are derived. There are four varieties of it, the Tanitic, the Pelusiac, the Butic, and the Tentyritic—so called from the various districts in which they are respectively grown. The upper part of Egypt, in the vicinity of Arabia, produces a shrub, known by some as "gossypium," but by most persons as "xylon"; hence the name of "xylina," given to the tissues that are manufactured from it. The shrub is small and bears a fruit similar in appearance to a nut with a beard, containing in the inside a silky substance, the down of which is spun into threads. There is no tissue known that is superior to those made from this thread, either for whiteness, softness, or dressing: the most esteemed vestments worn by the priests of Egypt are made of it. There is a fourth kind of tissue known by the name of "othoninum" which is made from a kind of marsh-reed, the panicule only being employed for the purpose. In Asia there is a thread made from broom which is employed in the construction of fishing nets, being found to be remarkably durable; for the purpose of preparing it the shrub is steeped in water for ten days. The Æthiopians and the people of India prepare a kind of thread from a fruit which resembles our apple, and the Arabians, from gourds that grow upon trees.

The Mode of Preparing Flax

In our part of the world the ripeness of flax is usually ascertained by two signs, the swelling of the seed, and
its assuming a yellowish tint. It is then pulled up by the
roots, made up into small sheaves that will just fill the hand,
and hung to dry in the sun. It is suspended with the roots
upwards the first day, and then for the five following days
the heads of the sheaves are placed, reclining one against
the other, in such a way that the seed which drops out
may fall into the middle. Linseed is employed for various
medicinal purposes and it is used by the country people of
Italy beyond the Padus in a certain kind of food which is
remarkable for its sweetness: for this long time past, however, it has only been in general use for sacrifices offered to
the divinities. After the wheat harvest is over, the stalks of
flax are plunged in water that has been warmed in the sun
and are then submitted to pressure with a weight; for there
is nothing known that is more light and buoyant than this.
When the outer coat is loosened it is a sign that the stalks
have been sufficiently steeped; after which they are again
turned with the heads downwards and left to dry as before
in the sun: when thoroughly dried they are beaten with
a tow mallet on a stone.

The part that lies nearest to the outer coat is known
by the name of "stuppa"; it is a flax of inferior quality and
is mostly employed for making the wicks of lamps. This,
however, requires to be combed out with iron hatchels
until the whole of the outer skin is removed. The inner
part presents numerous varieties of flax, esteemed respectively in proportion to their whiteness and their softness.
Spinning flax is held to be an honorable employment for
men: the husks, or outer coats, are employed for heating furnaces and ovens. There is a certain amount of skill required
in hatcheling flax and dressing it: it is a fair proportion for

fifty pounds in the sheaf to yield fifteen pounds of flax combed out. When spun into thread it is rendered additionally supple by being soaked in water and then beaten out upon a stone; and after it is woven into a tissue it is again beaten with heavy maces: indeed, the more roughly it is treated the better it is.

Linen Made of Asbestos

There has been invented also a kind of linen which is incombustible by flame. It is generally known as "live" linen, and I have seen napkins that were made of it thrown into a blazing fire in the room where the guests were at table, and after the stains were burnt out, come forth from the flames whiter and cleaner than they could possibly have been rendered by the aid of water. It is from this material that the corpse-cloths of monarchs are made, to ensure the separation of the ashes of the body from those of the pile. This substance grows in the deserts of India, scorched by the burning rays of the sun: here, where no rain is ever known to fall, and amid multitudes of deadly serpents, it becomes habituated to resist the action of fire. Rarely to be found, it presents considerable difficulties in weaving it into a tissue in consequence of its shortness; its color is naturally red and it only becomes white through the agency of fire. By those who find it it is sold at prices equal to those given for the finest pearls; by the Greeks it is called "asbestinon," a name which indicates its peculiar properties. Anaxilaüs makes a statement to the effect that if a tree is surrounded with linen made of this substance the noise of the blows given by the axe will be deadened thereby and that the tree may be cut down without their being heard. For these qualities it is that this linen occupies the very highest rank among all the kinds that are known.

At What Period Linen Was First Dyed

Attempts have even been made to dye linen and to make it assume the frivolous colors of our cloths. This was first done in the fleet of Alexander the Great, while sailing upon the river Indus; for upon one occasion, during a battle that was being fought, his generals and captains distinguished their vessels by the various tints of their sails, and astounded the people on the shores by giving their many colors to the breeze as it impelled them on. It was with sails of purple that Cleopatra accompanied M. Antonius to the battle of Actium, and it was by their aid that she took to flight: such being the distinguishing mark of the royal ship.

Colored Awnings

In more recent times linens alone have been employed for the purpose of affording shade in our theaters; Q. Catulus having been the first who applied them to this use on the occasion of the dedication by him of the Capitol. At a later period Lentulus Spinther, it is said, was the first to spread awnings of fine linen over the theater at the celebration of the Games in honor of Apollo. After this, Cæsar, when Dictator, covered with a linen awning the whole of the Roman Forum as well as the Sacred Way from his own house as far as the ascent to the Capitol, a sight, it is said, more wonderful even than the show of gladiators which he then exhibited. At a still later period and upon the occasion of no public games, Marcellus the son of Octavia, sister of Augustus, during his ædileship and in the eleventh consulship of his uncle, on the * * * day before the calends of August covered in the Forum with awnings, his object being to consult the health of those assembled there for the purposes of litigation—a vast change from the manners prevalent in the days of Cato the Censor who expressed a wish that the Forum was paved with nothing else but sharp pointed stones.

Awnings have been lately extended by the aid of ropes over the amphitheatres of the Emperor Nero, dyed azure like the heavens and bespangled all over with stars. Those which are employed by us to cover the inner court of our houses are generally red: one reason for employing them is to protect the moss that grows there from the rays of the sun. In other respects, white fabrics of linen have always held the ascendancy in public estimation.

Silkworms

These insects weave webs similar to those of the spider, the material of which is used for making the more costly and luxurious garments of females, known as "bombycina." Pamphile, a woman of Cos, the daughter of Platea, was the first person who discovered the art of unraveling these webs and spinning a tissue therefrom; indeed she ought not to be deprived of the glory of having discovered the art of making vestments which, while they cover a woman, at the same moment reveal her naked charms.

The silkworm is said to be a native of the isle of Cos where the vapors of the earth give new life to the flowers of the cypress, the terebinth, the ash, and the oak which have been beaten down by the showers. At first they assume the appearance of small butterflies with naked bodies but soon after, being unable to endure the cold, they throw out bristly hairs and assume quite a thick coat against the winter by rubbing off the down that covers the leaves by the aid of the roughness of their feet. This they compress into balls by carding it with their claws and then draw it out and hang it between the branches of the trees making it fine by combing it out as it were: last of all they take and roll it round their body, thus forming a nest in which they are enveloped. It is in this state that they are taken; after which they are placed in earthen vessels in a warm place and fed upon bran. A peculiar sort of down soon shoots forth upon the body, on being clothed with which they are sent to work upon another task. The cocoons which they have begun to form are rendered soft and pliable by the aid of water and are then drawn out into threads by means of a spindle made of a reed. Nor, in fact, have men felt ashamed to make use of garments formed of this material.

Section VI
THE JEWEL BOX

Rings

In this, as in every other case, luxury has introduced various fashions, either by adding to rings gems of exquisite brilliancy and so loading the fingers with whole revenues or else by engraving them with various devices: so that it is in one instance the workmanship, in another the material, that constitutes the real value of the ring. Then in the case of other gems, luxury has deemed it no less than sacrilege to make even a mark upon them and has caused them to be set whole, that no one may suppose that the ring was ever intended to be employed as a signet. In other instances luxury has willed that certain stones, on the side that is concealed by the finger, should not be closed in with gold, thus making gold of less account than thousands of tiny pebbles. On the other hand many persons will admit of no gems being set in their rings, but impress their seal with the gold itself, an invention which dates from the reign of Claudius Cæsar. At the present day the very slaves encase their iron rings with gold (while other articles belonging to them, they decorate with pure gold), a license which first originated in the Isle of Samothrace.

It was the custom at first to wear rings on a single finger, the one that is next to the little finger; and this we see the case in the statues of Numa and Servius Tullius. In later times it became the practice to put rings on the finger next to the thumb, even in the case of the statues of the gods; and more recently it has been the fashion to wear them upon the little finger as well. Among the peoples of Gallia and Britannia the middle finger, it is said, is used for this purpose. At the present day, among us, this is the only finger that is excepted, all the others being loaded with rings, smaller rings even being separately adapted for the smaller joints of the fingers. Some there are who heap several rings upon the little finger alone; while others wear but one ring upon this finger, the ring that sets a seal upon the signet-ring itself, this last being kept carefully shut up as an object of rarity too precious to be worn in common use and only to be taken from the cabinet as from a sanctuary. And thus is the wearing of a single ring upon the little finger no more than an ostentatious advertisement that the owner has property of a more precious nature under seal at home!

Some make a parade of the weight of their rings, while to others it is quite a labor to wear more than one at a time: some, in their solicitude for the safety of their gems, make the hoop of gold tinsel and fill it with a lighter material than gold, thinking thereby to diminish the risks of a fall. Others are in the habit of enclosing poisons beneath the stones of their rings, and so wear them as instruments of death. Demosthenes, for instance, that greatest of the orators of Greece, wore such a ring.

Other Uses Made of Gold

To honor the gods at their sacrifices, no greater mark of honor has been thought of than to gild the horns of the animals sacrificed—that is, of the larger victims only. But in warfare this species of luxury made such rapid advances that in the Epistles of M. Brutus from the Plains of Philippi we find expressions of indignation at the fibulæ of gold that were worn by the tribunes. Yes, so it is, by Hercules! and yet you, the same Brutus, have not said a word about women wearing gold upon their feet; while we, on the other hand, charge him with criminality who was the first to confer dignity upon gold by wearing the ring. Let men, at the present day, wear gold upon the arms in form of bracelets—known as "dardania," because the practice first originated in Dardania and called "virolæ" in the language of the

Celts, "viriæ" in that of Celtiberia; let women wear gold upon their arms and all their fingers, their necks, their ears, the tresses of their hair; let chains of gold run meandering along their sides; and in the still hours of the night let sachets filled with pearls hang suspended from the necks of their mistresses, all bedizened with gold, so that in their very sleep they may still retain the consciousness that they are the possessors of such gems: but are they to cover their feet as well with gold, and so, between the stola of the matrons and the garb of the plebeians establish an intermediate or equestrian order of females? Much more becomingly do we accord this distinction to our pages, and the adored beauty of these youths has quite changed the features of our public baths.

At the present day a fashion has been introduced among the men of wearing effigies upon their fingers representing Harpocrates and other divinities of Egypt. In the reign of Claudius there was introduced another unusual distinction, in the case of those to whom was granted the right of free admission, that, namely, of wearing the likeness of the emperor engraved in gold upon a ring: a circumstance that gave rise to vast numbers of informations, until the timely elevation of the Emperor Vespasianus rendered them impossible, by proclaiming that the right of admission to the emperor belonged equally to all.

Diamonds

The substance that possesses the greatest value, not only among the precious stones, but of all human possessions, is adamas, a mineral which for a long time was known to kings only, and to very few of them. Such was the name given to a nodosity of gold, sometimes, though but rarely, found in the mines in close proximity with gold, and only there to be found, it was thought. The ancients supposed that adamas was only to be discovered in the mines of

Æthiopia between the Temple of Mercury and the island of Meroë; and they have informed us that it was never larger than a cucumber seed, or differing at all from it in color.

At the present day, for the first time, there are no less than six different varieties of it recognized. The Indian adamas is found, not in a stratum of gold, but in a substance of a kindred nature to crystal; which it closely resembles in its transparency and its highly polished hexangular and hexahedral form. In shape it is turbinated, running to a point at either extremity, and closely resembling, marvelous to think of, two cones united at the base. In size it is as large even as a hazelnut. Resembling that of India is the adamas of Arabia which is found in a similar bed, but not so large in size. Other varieties have a pallid hue like that of silver and are only to be found in the midst of gold of the very finest quality. These stones are tested upon the anvil, and will resist the blow to such an extent as to make the iron rebound and the very anvil split asunder. Indeed its hardness is beyond all expression, while at the same time it quite sets fire at defiance and is incapable of being heated; owing to which indomitable powers it is that it has received the name which it derives from the Greek.

One kind, about as large as a grain of millet in size, has been called "cenchros," and another that is found in the gold mines at Philippi is known as the "Macedonian" adamas: this last is about as large as a cucumber seed in size. We next come to the Cyprian adamas, so called from its being found in the Isle of Cyprus: it is of a color somewhat inclining to that of copper, but, in medicinal virtues it is the most efficacious of them all.

Now with reference to those affinities and repugnances which exist between certain objects, known to the Greeks as "sympathia" and "antipathia," they nowhere manifest themselves with greater distinctness than here. This indomitable power, in fact, which sets at nought the two most violent agents in Nature, fire and iron, is made to yield be-

fore the blood of a he-goat. The blood must be no otherwise than fresh and warm; the stone, too, must be well
steeped in it and then subjected to repeated blows: and
even then it is apt to break both anvils and hammers of iron
if they are not of the very finest temper.

When this stone does happen to be broken, it divides
into fragments so minute as to be almost imperceptible.
These particles are held in great request by engravers, who
enclose them in iron and are enabled thereby, with the greatest facility, to cut the very hardest substances known. So
great is the antipathy borne by this stone to the magnet that
when placed near it will not allow of its attracting iron; or
if the magnet has already attracted the iron it will seize the
metal and drag it away from the other. Adamas overcomes
and neutralizes poisons, dispels delirium, and banishes
groundless perturbations of the mind; hence it is that some
have given it the name of "anachites." Metrodorus of
Scepsis is the only author that I know of who says that this
stone is found also in Germany and in the island of Basilia,
where amber is found. He says, too, that this is preferable
to the stone of Arabia; but can there be any doubt that his
statement is incorrect?

Pearl Oysters

The fish, as soon as ever it perceives the hand, shuts
its shell and covers up its treasures, being well aware that it
is for them that it is sought; and if it happens to catch the
hand it cuts it off with the sharp edge of the shell. And
no punishment is there that could be more justly inflicted.
There are other penalties added as well, seeing that the
greater part of these pearls are only to be found among rocks
and crags, while on the other hand those which lie out in the
main sea are generally accompanied by sea dogs. And yet,
for all this, the women will not banish these gems from their
ears! Some writers say that these animals live in communi-

ties, just like swarms of bees, each of them being governed by one remarkable for its size and its venerable old age, while at the same time it is possessed of marvelous skill in taking all due precautions against danger; the divers, they say, take special care to find these, and when once they are taken the others stray to and fro and are easily caught in their nets. We learn also that as soon as they are taken they are placed under a thick layer of salt in earthenware vessels; as the flesh is gradually consumed certain knots which form the pearls are disengaged from their bodies and fall to the bottom of the vessel.

The Various Kinds of Pearls

There is no doubt that pearls wear with use, and will change their color if neglected. All their merit consists in their whiteness, large size, roundness, polish, and weight; qualities which are not easily to be found united in the same; so much so, indeed, that no two pearls are ever found perfectly alike; and it was from this circumstance, no doubt, that our Roman luxury first gave them the name of 'unio," or the unique gem: for a similar name is not given them by the Greeks; nor, indeed, among the barbarians by whom they are found are they called anything else but "margaritæ." Even in the very whiteness of the pearl there is a great difference to be observed. Those are of a much clearer water that are found in the Red Sea, while the Indian pearl resembles in tint the scales of the mirror-stone, but exceeds all the others in size. The color that is most highly prized of all is that of those which are called alum-colored pearls. Long pearls also have their peculiar value; those are called "elenchi," which are of a long tapering shape, resembling our alabaster boxes in form and ending in a full bulb. Our ladies quite glory in having these suspended from their fingers, or two or three of them dangling from their ears. For the purpose of ministering to

these luxurious tastes there are various names and wearisome
refinements which have been devised by profuseness and
prodigality; for after inventing these earrings they have
given them the name of "crotalia," or castanet pendants, as
though quite delighted even with the rattling of the pearls
as they knock against each other; and now at the present day
the poorer classes are affecting them, as people are in the habit
of saying that "a pearl worn by a woman in public is as
good as a lictor walking before her." Nay, even more than
this, they put them on their feet, and not only on the lace
of their sandals but all over the shoes; it is not enough to
wear pearls but they must tread upon them and walk with
them under foot as well.

Pearls used formerly to be found in our sea, but more
frequently about the Thracian Bosporus; they were of a
red color and small and enclosed in a shellfish known by
the name of "myes."

It is quite clear that the interior of the pearl is solid
as no fall is able to break it. Pearls are not always found in the
middle of the body of the animal, but sometimes in one
place, and sometimes another. Indeed I have seen some
which lay at the edge of the shell just as though in the very
act of coming forth, and in some fishes as many as four or
five. Up to the present time very few have been found
which exceeded half an ounce in weight. It is a well-ascertained fact that in Britannia pearls are found, though small
and of a bad color; for the deified Julius Cæsar wished it
to be distinctly understood that the breastplate which he
dedicated to Venus Genetrix in her temple was made of
British pearls.

I once saw Lollia Paulina, the wife of the Emperor Caius—it was not at any public festival, or any
solemn ceremonial, but only at an ordinary wedding entertainment—covered with emeralds and pearls which shone in
alternate layers upon her head, in her hair, in her wreaths, in
her ears, upon her neck, in her bracelets, and on her fingers.

and the value of which amounted in all to forty millions of sesterces; indeed she was prepared at once to prove the fact by showing the receipts and acquittances.

Emeralds

There is no stone the color of which is more delightful to the eye; for whereas the sight fixes itself with avidity upon the green grass and the foliage of the trees, we have all the more pleasure in looking upon the smaragdus, there being no green in existence of a more intense color than this. And then, besides, of all the precious stones this is the only one that feeds the sight without satiating it. Even when the vision has been fatigued with intently viewing other objects it is refreshed by being turned upon this stone; and lapidaries know of nothing that is more gratefully soothing to the eyes, its soft green tints being wonderfully adapted for assuaging lassitude, when felt in those organs.

And when viewed from a distance these stones appear all the larger to the sight, reflecting as they do their green hues upon the circumambient air. Neither sunshine, shade, nor artificial light effects any change in their appearance; they have always a softened and graduated brilliancy; and transmitting the light with facility, they allow the vision to penetrate their interior; a property which is so pleasing, also, with reference to water. In form they are mostly concave, so as to reunite the rays of light and the powers of vision: and hence it is that it is so universally agreed upon among mankind to respect these stones and to forbid their surface to be engraved. In the case, however, of the stones of Scythia and Egypt their hardness is such that it would be quite impossible to penetrate them. When the surface of the smaragdus is flat it reflects the image of objects in the same manner as a mirror. The Emperor Nero used to view the combats of the gladiators upon a smaragdus.

Opals

Opals only yield to the smaragdus in value. India is the sole parent of these precious stones, thus completing her glory as being the great producer of the most costly gems. Of all precious stones, opal presents the greatest difficulties of description, it displaying at once the piercing fire of carbunculus, the purple brilliancy of amethystos, and the sea-green of smaragdus, the whole blended together and refulgent with a brightness that is quite incredible. Some authors have compared the effect of its refulgence to that of the color known as Armenian pigment, while others speak of it as resembling the flame of burning sulphur, or of flame fed with oil. In size the opal is about as large as a hazelnut and, with reference to it, there is a remarkable historical anecdote related. For there is still in existence a stone of this class, on account of which Antonius proscribed the senator Nonius, son of the Nonius Struma whom the poet Catullus was so displeased at seeing in the curule chair, and grandfather of the Servilius Nonianus who in our own times was consul. On being thus proscribed, Nonius took to flight, carrying with him out of all his wealth, nothing but this ring, the value of which, it is well known, was estimated at two millions of sesterces.

Amber

From Carnuntum in Pannonia to the coasts of Germany from which the amber is brought is a distance of about six hundred miles, a fact which has been only very recently ascertained; and there is still living a member of the equestrian order who was sent thither by Julianus, the manager of the gladiatorial exhibitions for the Emperor Nero, to procure a supply of this article. Traversing the coasts of that country and visiting the various markets there he brought back amber in such vast quantities as to admit of the nets, which are used for protecting the podium against the wild beasts, being studded with amber.

The arms too, the litters, and all the other apparatus, were on one day decorated with nothing but amber, a different kind of display being made each day that these spectacles were exhibited. The largest piece of amber that this personage brought to Rome was thirteen pounds in weight.

That amber is found in India too, is a fact well ascertained. Archelaüs who reigned over Cappadocia says that it is brought from that country in the rough state and with the fine bark still adhering to it, it being the custom there to polish it by boiling it in the grease of a sucking pig. One great proof that amber must have been originally in a liquid state is the fact that, owing to its transparency, certain objects are to be seen within, ants for example, gnats, and lizards. These, no doubt, must have first adhered to it while liquid and then, upon its hardening, have remained enclosed within.

There are several kinds of amber. The white is the one that has the finest odor, but neither this nor the wax-colored amber is held in very high esteem. The red amber is more highly valued; and still more so when it is transparent, without presenting too brilliant and igneous an appearance. For amber, to be of high quality, should present a brightness like that of fire, but not flakes resembling those of flame. The most highly esteemed amber is that known as the "Falernian," from its resemblance to the color of Falernian wine; it is perfectly transparent and has a softened, transparent, brightness. Other kinds are valued for their mellowed tints, like the color of boiled honey in appearance. It ought to be known, however, that any color can be imparted to amber that may be desired, it being sometimes stained with kid suet and root of alkanet; indeed at the present day amber is dyed purple. When a vivifying heat has been imparted to it by rubbing it between the fingers, amber will attract chaff, dried leaves, and thin bark, just in the same way that the magnet attracts iron. Piece of amber steeped in oil burn with a more brilliant and more lasting flame than pith of flax.

So highly valued is this as an object of luxury, that a very diminutive human effigy made of amber has been known to sell at a higher price than living men in stout and vigorous health. This single ground for censure, however, is far from being sufficient; in Corinthian objects of vertu, it is the copper that recommends them, combined with silver and gold; and in embossed works it is the skill and genius of the artist that is so highly esteemed. We have already said that pearls are of use for wearing upon the head and gems upon the fingers. In the case of all other luxuries, it is either a spirit of ostentation or some utility that has been discovered in them that pleads so strongly in their behalf; but in that of amber we have solely the consciousness that we are enjoying a luxury, and nothing more.

Section VII
TOILETRIES

Perfumes

There are two elements which enter into the composition of unguents, the juices and the solid parts. The former generally consist of various kinds of oils, the latter of odoriferous substances. These last are known as hedysmata, while the oils are called stymmata. There is a third element which occupies a place between the two but has been much neglected, the coloring matter, namely. To produce a color cinnabar and alkanet are often employed. If salt is sprinkled in the oil it will aid it in retaining its properties; but if alkanet has been employed, salt is never used. Resin and gum are added to fix the odor in the solid perfumes; indeed it is apt to die away and disappear with the greatest rapidity if these substances are not employed.

Among the most common unguents at the present day, and for that reason supposed to be the most ancient, is that composed of oil of myrtle, calamus, cypress, cyprus, mastich, and pomegranate rind. I am of opinion that the unguents which have been the most universally adopted are those which are compounded of the rose, a flower that grows everywhere; and hence for a long time the composition of oil of roses was of the most simple nature, though more recently there have been added omphacium, rose blossoms, cinnabar, calamus, honey, sweet-rush, flour of salt or else alkanet, and wine. The same is the case with oil of saffron, to which have been lately added cinnabar, alkanet, and wine; and with oil of sampsuchum, with which omphacium and calamus have been compounded. The best comes from Cyprus and Mitylene, where sampsuchum abounds in large quantities.

The commoner kinds of oil are mixed with those of

63

myrrh and laurel, to which are added sampsuchum, lilies, fenugreek, myrrh, cassia, nard, sweet-rush, and cinnamon. There is an oil, too, made of the common quince and the sparrow quince, called melinum; it is used as an ingredient in unguents, mixed with omphacium, oil of cyprus, oil of sesamum, balsamum, sweet-rush, cassia, and abrotonum.

Those unguents which are known by the name of "diapasma," are composed of dried perfumes. The lees of unguents are known by the name of "magma." In all these preparations the most powerful perfume is the one that is added the last of all. Unguents keep best in boxes of alabaster, and perfumes when mixed with oil, which conduces all the more to their durability the thicker it is, such as the oil of almonds for instance. Unguents improve with age; but the sun is apt to spoil them, for which reason they are usually stowed away in a shady place in vessels of lead. When their goodness is being tested they are placed on the back of the hand, lest the heat of the palm, which is more fleshy, should have a bad effect upon them.

Perfumes form the objects of a luxury which may be looked upon as being the most superfluous of any, for pearls and jewels do pass to a man's representative, and garments have some durability; but unguents lose their odor in an instant and die away the very hour they are used. The very highest recommendation of them is that when a female passes by the odor which proceeds from her may possibly attract the attention of those who till then are intent upon something else. In price they exceed so large a sum as four hundred denarii per pound: so vast is the amount that is paid for a luxury made not for our own enjoyment but for that of others; for the person who carries the perfume about him is not the one, after all, that smells it.

And yet even here there are some points of difference that deserve to be remarked. We read in the works of Cicero that those unguents which smell of the earth are preferable to those which smell of saffron; being a proof that even in a matter which most strikingly bespeaks our state of extreme corruptness it is thought as well to temper the vice by a little show of austerity. There are some persons too who look more particularly for consistency in their unguents, to which they accordingly give the name of "spissum"; thus showing that they love not only to be sprinkled but even to be plastered over with unguents. We have known the very soles of the feet to be sprinkled with perfumes; a refinement which was taught, it is said, by M. Otho to the Emperor Nero. How, I should like to know, could a perfume be at all perceptible, or productive of any kind of pleasure when placed on that part of the body? We have heard also a private person giving orders for the walls of the bathroom to be sprinkled with unguents, while the Emperor Caius had the same thing done to his sitting bath: that this might not be looked upon as the peculiar privilege of a prince, it was afterwards done by one of the slaves that belonged to Nero.

But the most wonderful thing of all is that this kind of luxurious gratification should have made its way into the camp: at all events, the eagles and the standards, dusty as they are and bristling with their sharpened points, are anointed on festive days. I only wish it could by any possibility be stated who it was that first taught us this practice. It was, no doubt, under the corrupting influence of such temptations as these that our eagles achieved the conquest of the world: thus do we seek to obtain their patronage and sanction for our vices, and make them our precedent for using unguents even beneath the casque.

I cannot exactly say at what period the use of unguents first found its way to Rome. It is a well-known fact that when King Antiochus and Asia were subdued, an edict was published in the year of the City 565, in the censorship of P. Licinius Crassus and L. Julius Cæsar, forbidding any one to sell exotics; for by that name unguents were then called. But, in the name of Hercules! at the present day there are some persons who even go so far as to put them in their drink, and the bitterness produced thereby is prized to a degree, in order that by their lavishness on these odors they may thus gratify the senses of two parts of the body at the same moment.

Milk Baths

Asses' milk is thought to be very efficacious in whitening the skin: at all events, Poppaea, the wife of Nero, used always to have with her five hundred asses with foal, and used to bathe the whole of her body with their milk.

Depilatories

Bats' blood has all the virtues of a depilatory: but if applied to the cheeks of youths, it will not be found sufficiently efficacious, unless it is immediately followed up by an application of verdigrease or hemlock seed; this method having the effect of entirely removing the hair, or at least reducing it to the state of a fine down. It is generally thought, too, that bats' brains are productive of a similar effect; there being two kinds of these brains, the red and the white. Some persons mix with the brains the blood and liver of the same animal: others boil down a viper in three semi-sextarii of oil and, after boning it, use it as a depilatory, first pulling out the hairs that are wanted not to grow. The gall of a hedgehog is a depilatory, more particularly if mixed with bats' brains and goats' milk: the ashes, too, of a burnt hedgehog are used for a similar purpose. If after plucking out the hairs that are wanted not to grow, or if before they make their appearance, the parts are well rubbed with the milk of a bitch with her first litter no hairs will grow there. The same result is ensured, it is said, by using the blood of a tick taken from off a dog, or else the blood or gall of a swallow.

Ants' eggs, they say, beaten up with flies, impart a black color to the eyebrows. If it is considered desirable that the color of the infant's eyes should be black the pregnant woman must eat a rat. Ashes of burnt earthworms, applied with oil, prevent the hair from turning white.

Section VIII
INTERIORS

Plaster

In the ancient laws for the regulation of building, no contractor was to use mortar less than three months old; hence it is that no cracks have disfigured the plaster coatings of their walls. These stuccos will never present a sufficiently bright surface unless there have been three layers of sanded mortar and two of marbled mortar upon that. In damp localities and places subject to exhalations from the sea it is the best plan to substitute ground earthenware mortar for sanded mortar. In Greece it is the practice first to pound the lime and sand used for plastering with wooden pestles in a large trough. The test by which it is known that marbled mortar has been properly blended is its not adhering to the trowel; whereas if it is only wanted for whitewashing, the lime, after being well slaked with water, should stick like glue. For this last purpose the lime should only be slaked in lumps.

At Elis there is a Temple of Minerva which was pargetted, they say, by Panænus the brother of Phidias with a mortar that was blended with milk and saffron: hence it is that even at the present day, when rubbed with spittle on the finger, it yields the smell and flavor of saffron.

Experience has proved that the best plaster of all is that prepared from specular stone, or any other stone that is similarly laminated. Gypsum when moistened must be used immediately, as it hardens with the greatest rapidity; it admits however of being triturated over again and so reduced to powder. It is very useful for pargetting and has a pleasing effect when used for ornamental figures and wreaths in buildings.

There is one remarkable fact connected with this

substance; Caius Proculeius an intimate friend of the Emperor Augustus, suffering from violent pains in the stomach, swallowed gypsum and so put an end to his existence.

Pavements

Pavements are an invention of the Greeks, who also practiced the art of painting them, till they were superseded by mosaics. In this last branch of art the highest excellence has been attained by Sosus who laid at Pergamus the mosaic pavement known as the "Asarotos œcos"; from the fact that he there represented in small squares of different colors the remnants of a banquet lying upon the pavement and other things which are usually swept away with the broom, they having all the appearance of being left there by accident. There is a dove also, greatly admired, in the act of drinking and throwing the shadow of its head upon the water; while other birds are to be seen sunning and pluming themselves on the margin of a drinking bowl.

The first pavements, in my opinion, were those now known to us as barbaric and subtegulan pavements, a kind of work that was beaten down with the rammer: at least if we may form a judgment from the name that has been given to them. The first diamonded pavement at Rome was laid in the Temple of Jupiter Capitolinus after the commencement of the Third Punic War.

We must not omit here one other kind of pavement, that known as the "Græcanic." The ground is well rammed down, and a bed of rough work or broken pottery is then laid upon it. Upon the top of this a layer of charcoal is placed, well trodden down with a mixture of sand, lime, and ashes; care being taken, by line and rule, to give it a uniform thickness of half a foot. The surface then presents the ordinary appearance of the ground; but if it is well rubbed with the polishing stone it will have all the appearance of a black pavement.

Mosaic pavements were first introduced in the time of Sylla; at all events there is still in existence a pavement, formed of small segments, which he ordered to be laid down in the Temple of Fortune at Præneste. Since his time these mosaics have left the ground for the arched roofs of houses, and they are now made of glass. This is but a recent invention; for there can be no doubt that, when Agrippa ordered the earthenware walls of the hot baths in the Thermæ which he was building at Rome to be painted in encaustic, and had the other parts coated with pargetting, he would have had the arches decorated with mosaics in glass if the use of them had been known; or, at all events, if glass had by that time come to be used for the arched roofs of apartments.

Glass

In Syria there is a region known as Phœnice, adjoining to Judæa and enclosing, between the lower ridges of Mount Carmelus, a marshy district known by the name of Cendebia. In this district, it is supposed, rises the river Belus which, after a course of five miles, empties itself into the sea near the colony of Ptolemaïs. The tide of this river is sluggish and the water unwholesome to drink, but held sacred for the observance of certain religious ceremonials. Full of slimy deposits and very deep it is only at the reflux of the tide that the river discloses its sands; which, agitated by the waves, separate themselves from their impurities and so become cleansed. It is generally thought that it is the acridity of the sea-water that has this purgative effect upon the sand and that without this action no use could be made of it. The shore upon which this sand is gathered is not more than half a mile in extent; and yet for many ages this was the only spot that afforded the material for making glass.

The story is that a ship laden with niter, being moored upon this spot, the merchants while preparing their repast upon the seashore, finding no stones at hand for supporting their cauldrons, employed for the purpose some lumps of niter which they had taken from the vessel. Upon its being subjected to the action of the fire, in combination with the sand of the seashore, they beheld transparent streams flowing forth of a liquid hitherto unknown: this, it is said, was the origin of glass.

In process of time, as human industry is ingenious in discovering, it was not content with the combination of niter, but magnet stone began to be added as well; from the impression that it attracts liquefied glass as well as iron. In a similar manner brilliant stones of various descriptions came to be added in the melting and, at last, shells and fossil sand. Some authors tell us that the glass of India is made of broken crystal and that, in consequence, there is none that can be compared to it.

In fusing it, light and dry wood is used for fuel, Cyprian copper and niter being added to the melting, niter of Ophir more particularly. It is melted like copper in contiguous furnaces, and a swarthy mass of an unctuous appearance is the result. Of such a penetrating nature is the molten glass that it will cut to the very bone any part of the body which it may come near, and that, too, before it is even felt. This mass is again subjected to fusion in the furnace for the purpose of coloring it; after which the glass is either blown into various forms, turned in a lathe, or engraved like silver. Sidon was formerly famous for its glasshouses, for it was this place that first invented mirrors.

Such was the ancient method of making glass; but at the present day there is found a very white sand for the purpose, at the mouth of the river Volturnus in Italy. It spreads over an extent of six miles upon the seashore that lies between Cumæ and Liternum and is prepared for use by pounding it with a pestle and mortar; which done, it is mixed with three parts of niter, either by weight or measure, and when fused is transferred to another furnace. Here it forms a mass of what is called "hammonitrum"; which is again submitted to fusion and becomes a mass of pure, white,

glass. Indeed at the present day throughout the Gallic and
Spanish provinces we find sand subjected to a similar process.
In the reign of Tiberius, it is said, a combination was devised
which produced a flexible glass; but the manufactory of the
artist was totally destroyed, we are told, in order to prevent
the value of copper, silver, and gold, from becoming depre-
ciated. This story was for a long time more widely spread
than well authenticated. But be it as it may, it is of little
consequence; for in the time of the Emperor Nero there
was a process discovered by which two small glass cups were
made of the kind called "petroti," the price of which was
no less than six thousand sesterces!

Obsian Glass and Obsian Stone

Among the various kinds of glass we may also reckon
Obsian glass, a substance very similar to the stone which
Obsius discovered in Æthiopia. This stone is of a very
dark color and sometimes transparent; but it is dull to the
sight and reflects, when attached as a mirror to walls,
the shadow of the object rather than the image. Many persons
use it for jewelry, and I myself have seen solid statues in this
material of the late Emperor Augustus, of very considerable thickness. That prince consecrated in the Temple of
Concord, as something marvelous, four figures of elephants
made of Obsian stone. Tiberius Cæsar restored to the people
of Heliopolis, as an object of ceremonial worship, an image in this stone which had been found among the property left by one of the præfects of Egypt. It was a figure
of Menelaüs; a circumstance which goes far towards prov-
ing that the use of this material is of more ancient date
than is generally supposed, confounded as it is at the present
day with glass by reason of its resemblance. Xenocrates
says that Obsian stone is found in India also and in Sam-
nium in Italy; and that it is a natural product of Spain, upon
the coasts which border on the Ocean.

There is an artificial Obsian stone made of colored glass for services for the table; and there is also a glass that is red all through and opaque, known as "hæmatinum." A dead white glass is made, as also other kinds in imitation of murrhine color, hyacinthine, sapphire, and every other tint: indeed there is no material of a more pliable nature than this or better suited for coloring. However, the highest value is set upon glass that is entirely colorless and transparent, as nearly as possible resembling crystal. For drinking vessels, glass has quite superseded the use of silver and gold; but it is unable to stand heat unless a cold liquid is poured in first. And yet we find that globular glass vessels filled with water, when brought in contact with the rays of the sun, become heated to such a degree as to cause articles of clothing to ignite. When broken, glass admits of being joined by the agency of heat; but it cannot be wholly fused without being pulverized into small fragments, as we see done in the process of making the small checkers known as "abaculi," for mosaic work; some of which are of variegated colors and of different shapes. If glass is fused with sulphur it will become as hard as stone.

Murals

Ludius, who lived in the time of the late Emperor Augustus, must not be allowed to pass without some notice; for he was the first to introduce the fashion of covering the walls of our houses with most pleasing landscapes, representing villas, porticos, ornamental gardening, woods, groves, hills, fishponds, canals, rivers, seashores, and anything else one could desire; varied with figures of persons walking, sailing, or proceeding to their villas on asses or in carriages. Then too there are others to be seen fishing, fowling, or gathering in the vintage. In some of his decorations there are fine villas to be seen, and roads to them across the marshes, with women making bargains to be carried across on men's shoulders, who move along slipping at every step and tottering beneath their load; with numberless other subjects of a similar nature redolent of mirth and of the most amusing ingenuity. It was this artist who first decorated our uncovered edifices with representations of maritime cities, a subject which produces a most pleasing effect, and at a very trifling expense.

Silverwork

For this long time past it has been the fashion to plate the couches of our women, as well as some of our banqueting couches, entirely with silver. Carvilius Pollio a Roman of equestrian rank was the first, it is said, to adorn these last with silver; not, I mean, to plate them all over nor yet to make them after the Delian pattern; the Punic fashion being the one he adopted. It was after this last pattern that he had them ornamented with gold as well: and it was not long after his time that silver couches came into fashion, in imitation of the couches of Delos. All this extravagance was fully expiated by the civil wars of Sulla.

In fact it was but very shortly before that period that these couches were invented, as well as chargers of silver one hundred pounds in weight: of which last, it is a well-known fact, that there were then upwards of one hundred and fifty in Rome, and that many persons were proscribed through the devices of others who were desirous to gain possession thereof. Well may our Annals be put to the blush for having to impute those civil wars to the existence of such vices as these!

Our own age has waxed even stronger in this respect. In the reign of Claudius his slave Drusillanus, surnamed Rotundus, who acted as his steward in Nearer Spain possessed a silver charger weighing five hundred pounds, for the manufacture of which a workshop had to be expressly built. This charger was accompanied by eight other dishes, each two hundred and fifty pounds in weight. How many of his fellow slaves, pray, would it have taken to introduce these dishes, or who were to be the guests served therefrom?

Cornelius Nepos says that before the victory gained by Sylla there were but two banqueting couches adorned with silver at Rome, and that in his own recollection silver was first used for adorning sideboards. Fenestella, who died at the end of the reign of Tiberius Cæsar, informs us that at that period sideboards inlaid even with tortoiseshell had come into fashion; whereas a little before his time they had been made of solid wood of a round shape and not much larger than our tables. He says, however, that when he was a boy they had begun to make the sideboards square, and of different pieces of wood, or else veneered with maple or citrus: and that at a later period the fashion was introduced of overlaying the corners and the seams at the joinings with silver. The name given to them in his youth, he says, was "tympana"; and it was at this period that the chargers which had been known as "magides" by the ancients first received the name of "lances," from their resemblance to the scales of a balance.

Veneer

The best woods for employing as a veneer for covering others are the citrus, the terebinth, the different varieties of the maple, the box, the palm, the holly, the holm oak, the root of the elder, and the poplar. The alder furnishes also a kind of tuberosity which is cut into layers like those of the citrus and the maple. In all the other trees the tuberosities are of no value whatever. It is the central part of trees that is most variegated, and the nearer we approach to the root the smaller are the spots and the more wavy. It was this appearance that originated that requirement of luxury which displays itself in covering one tree with another and bestowing upon the more common woods a bark of higher price. In order to make a single tree sell many times over laminæ of veneer have been devised; but that was not thought sufficient—the horns of animals must next be stained of different colors and their teeth cut into sections in order to decorate wood with ivory and, at a later period, to veneer it all over. Then man must go and seek his materials in the sea as well! For this purpose he has learned to cut tortoiseshell into sections; and of late in the reign of Nero there was a monstrous invention devised of destroying its natural appearance by paint, and making it sell at a still higher price by a successful imitation of wood.

It is this way that the value of our couches is so greatly enhanced; it is in this way too that they bid the rich luster of the terebinth to be outdone, a mock citrus to be made that shall be more valuable than the real one, and the grain of the maple to be feigned. At one time luxury was content with wood; at the present day it sets us on buying tortoiseshell in the guise of wood.

Citrus Tables

There is preserved to the present day a table which belonged to M. Cicero, and for which, notwithstanding his comparatively moderate means, he gave no less than one million sesterces: we find mention made also of one belonging to Gallus Asinius, which cost one million one hundred thousand sesterces. Two tables were also sold by auction which had belonged to King Juba; the price fetched by one was one million two hundred thousand sesterces, and that of the other something less. There has been lately destroyed by fire a table which came down from the family of the Cathegi and which had been sold for the sum of one million four hundred thousand sesterces, the price of a considerable domain, if any one could be found who would give so large a sum for an estate.

The largest table that has ever yet been known was one that belonged to Ptolemæus, king of Mauretania; it was made of two semicircumferences joined together down the middle, being four feet and a half in diameter and a quarter of a foot in thickness: the most wonderful fact connected with it was the surprising skill with which the joining had been concealed, and which rendered it more valuable than if it had been by nature a single piece of wood. The largest table that is made of a single piece of wood is the one that takes its name from Nomius, a freedman of Tiberius Cæsar. The diameter of it is four feet, short by three quarters of an inch, and it is half a foot in thickness, less the same fraction. While speaking upon this subject I ought not to omit to mention that the Emperor Tiberius had a table that exceeded four feet in diameter by two inches and a quarter, and was an inch and a half in thickness: this however was only covered with a veneer of citrus wood, while that which belonged to his freedman Nomius was so costly, the whole material of which it was composed being knotted wood.

These knots are properly a disease or excrescence of the root, and those used for this purpose are more particularly esteemed which have lain entirely concealed under ground; they are much more rare than those that grow above ground and that are to be found on the branches also. Thus, to speak correctly, that which we buy at so vast a price is in reality a defect in the tree: of the size and root of it a notion may be easily formed from the circular sections of its trunk.

Section IX
PAPER

We have not as yet taken any notice of the marsh plants, nor yet of the shrubs that grow upon the banks of rivers: we must make some mention of the nature of the papyrus, seeing that all the usages of civilized life depend in such a remarkable degree upon the employment of paper—at all events the remembrance of past events. M. Varro informs us that paper owes its discovery to the victorious career of Alexander the Great, at the time when Alexandria in Egypt was founded by him; before which period paper had not been used, the leaves of the palm having been employed for writing at an early period, and after that the bark of certain trees. In succeeding ages public documents were inscribed on sheets of lead, while private memoranda were impressed upon linen cloths or else engraved on tablets of wax; indeed we find it stated in Homer that tablets were employed for this purpose even before the time of the Trojan war. It is generally supposed that the country which that poet speaks of as Egypt was not the same that is at present understood by that name, for the Sebennytic and the Saitic Nomes in which all the papyrus is produced have been added since his time by the alluvion of the Nile; indeed he himself has stated that the mainland was a day and a night's sail from the island of Pharos, which island at the present day is united by a bridge to the city of Alexandria. In later times, a rivalry having sprung up between King Ptolemy and King Eumenes, in reference to their respective libraries, Ptolemy prohibited the export of papyrus; upon which, as Varro relates, parchment was invented for a similar purpose at Pergamus. After this the use of that commodity by which immortality is ensured to man became universally known.

Papyrus grows either in the marshes of Egypt, or in

the sluggish waters of the river Nile when they have over-
flowed and are lying stagnant in pools that do not exceed
a couple of cubits in depth. The root lies obliquely and is
about the thickness of one's arm; the section of the stalk is
triangular and it tapers gracefully upwards towards the extremity, being not more than ten cubits at most in height.
Very much like a thyrsus in shape, it has a head on the top
which has no seed in it, and indeed is of no use whatever
except as a flower employed to crown the statues of the
gods. The natives use the roots by way of wood, not only
for firing but for various other domestic purposes as well.
From the papyrus itself they construct boats, and of the
outer coat they make sails and mats as well as cloths, besides
coverlets and ropes; they chew it, both raw and boiled,
though they swallow the juice only.

The papyrus grows in Syria also on the borders of the
same lake around which grows the sweet-scented calamus; and King Antiochus used to employ the productions
of that country solely as cordage for naval purposes; for the
use of spartum had not then become commonly known.
More recently it has been understood that a papyrus grows
in the river Euphrates in the vicinity of Babylon, from
which a similar kind of paper may easily be produced: however, up to the present time the Parthians have preferred to
impress their characters upon cloths.

Paper is made from the papyrus by splitting it with a
needle into very thin leaves, due care being taken that they
should be as broad as possible. That of the first quality is
taken from the center of the plant, and so in regular succession, according to the order of division. "Hieratica" was
the name that was anciently given to it, from the circumstance that it was entirely reserved for the religious books.
In later times, through a spirit of adulation, it received the
name of "Augusta," just as that of second quality was called
"Liviana" from his wife Livia; the consequence of which
was that the name "hieratica" came to designate that of only
third-rate quality. The paper of the next quality was called

"amphitheatrica," from the locality of its manufacture. The skillful manufactory that was established by Fannius at Rome was in the habit of receiving this last kind, and there, by a very careful process of insertion, it was rendered much finer; so much so, that from being a common sort, he made it a paper of first-rate quality and gave his own name to it: while that which was not subjected to this additional process retained its original name of "amphitheatrica." Next to this is the Saitic paper, so called from the city of that name where it is manufactured in very large quantities, though of cuttings of inferior quality. The Tæniotic paper, so called from a place in the vicinity, is manufactured from the materials that lie nearer to the outside skin; it is sold, not according to its quality, but by weight only. As to the paper that is known as "emporetica," it is quite useless for writing upon and is only employed for wrapping up other paper and as a covering for various articles of merchandise, whence its name, as being used by dealers. After this comes the bark of the papyrus, the outer skin of which bears a strong resemblance to the bulrush and is solely used for making ropes, and then only for those which have to go into the water.

All these various kinds of paper are made upon a table, moistened with Nile water; a liquid which, when in a muddy state, has the peculiar qualities of glue. This table being first inclined, the leaves of papyrus are laid upon it lengthwise, as long indeed as the papyrus will admit of, the jagged edges being cut off at either end; after which a cross layer is placed over it, the same way in fact that hurdles are made. When this is done the leaves are pressed close together and then dried in the sun; after which they are united to one another, the best sheets being always taken first and the inferior ones added afterwards. There are never more than twenty of these sheets to a roll.

There is a great difference in the breadth of the various kinds of paper. That of best quality is thirteen fingers wide, while the hieratics is two fingers less. The Fanniana is ten fingers wide, and that known as "amphitheatrica" one less. The Saitic is of still smaller breadth, indeed it is not so wide as the mallet with which the paper is beaten; and the emporetica is particularly narrow, being not more than six fingers in breadth.

In addition to the above particulars, paper is esteemed according to its fineness, its stoutness, its whiteness, and its smoothness. Claudius Cæsar effected a change in that which till then had been looked upon as being of the first quality: for the Augustan paper had been found to be so remarkably fine, as to offer no resistance to the pressure of the pen; in addition to which, as it allowed the writing upon it to run through, it was continually causing apprehensions of its being blotted and blurred by the writing on the other side; the remarkable transparency, too, of the paper was very unsightly to the eye. To obviate these inconveniences, a groundwork of paper was made with leaves of the second quality, over which was laid a woof, as it were, formed of leaves of the first. He increased the width also of paper; the width of the common sort being made a foot, and that of the size known as "macrocollum" a cubit; though one inconvenience was soon detected in it, for, upon a single leaf being torn in the press, more pages were apt to be spoilt than before. In consequence of the advantages abovementioned, the Claudian has come to be preferred to all other kinds of paper, though the Augustan is still used for the purposes of epistolary correspondence. The Livian, which had nothing in common with that of first quality but was entirely of a secondary rank, still holds its former place.

The roughness and inequalities in paper are smoothed down with a tooth or shell; but the writing in such places is very apt to fade. When it is thus polished the paper does not take the ink so readily but is of a more lustrous and shining surface. The water of the Nile that has been originally employed in its manufacture, being sometimes used without due precaution, will unfit the paper for taking writing: this fault may be detected by a blow with the mallet, or even by the smell when the carelessness has been extreme. These spots, too, may be detected by the eye; but the streaks that run down the middle of the leaves where they have been pasted together, though they render the paper spongy and of a soaking nature, can hardly ever be detected before the ink runs while the pen is forming the letters; so many are the openings for fraud to be put in practice. The consequence is that another labor has been added to the due preparation of paper.

The common paper paste is made of the finest flour of wheat mixed with boiling water, and some small drops of vinegar sprinkled in it: for the ordinary workman's paste or gum, if employed for this purpose will render the paper brittle. Those who take the greatest pains boil the crumb of leavened bread and then strain off the water: by the adoption of this method the paper has the fewest seams caused by the paste that lies between and is softer than the nap of linen. All kinds of paste that are used for this purpose ought not to be older or newer than one day. The paper is then thinned out with a mallet, after which a new layer of paste is placed upon it; then the creases which have formed are again pressed out and it then undergoes the same process with the mallet as before. It is thus that we have memorials preserved in the ancient handwriting of Tiberius and Caius Gracchus, which I have seen in the possession of Pomponius Secundus the poet, a very illustrious citizen, almost two hundred years since those characters were penned. As for the handwritings of Cicero, Augustus, and Virgil, we frequently see them at the present day.

There are some facts of considerable importance which make against the opinion expressed by M. Varro, relative to the invention of paper. Cassius Hemina, a writer of very great antiquity, has stated in the Fourth Book of his Annals, that Cneius Terentius the scribe, while engaged in digging on his land in the Janiculum, came to a coffer, in which Numa had been buried, the former king of Rome, and that in this coffer were also found some books of his. This took place in the consulship of Publius Cornelius Cathegus the son of Lucius, and of M. Bæbius Tamphilus the son of Quintus, the interval between whose consulship and the reign of Numa was five hundred and thirty-five years. These books were made of paper and, a thing that is more remarkable still, is the fact that they lasted so many years buried in the ground. In order to establish a fact of such singular importance, I shall here quote the words of Hemina himself—"Some persons expressed wonder how these books could have possibly lasted so long a time—this was the explanation that Terentius gave: 'In nearly the middle of the coffer there lay a square stone bound on every side with cords enveloped in wax; upon this stone the books had been placed and it was through this precaution, he thought, that they had not rotted. The books, too, were carefully covered with citrus leaves and it was through this, in his belief, that they had been protected from the attacks of worms.' In these books were written certain doctrines relative to the Pythagorean philosophy; they were burnt by Q. Petilius the prætor, because they treated of philosophical subjects."

Piso, who had formerly been censor, relates the same facts in the First Book of his Commentaries, but he states in addition that there were seven books on Pontifical Rights and seven on the Pythagorean philosophy. Tuditanus, in his Fourteenth Book, says that they contained the decrees of Numa: Varro, in the Seventh Book of his "Antiquities of Mankind," states that they were twelve in number; and Antias, in his Second Book, says that there were twelve written in Latin on pontifical matters, and as many in Greek containing philosophical precepts. The same author states also in his Third Book why it was thought proper to burn them.

It is a fact acknowledged by all writers that the Sibyl brought three books to Tarquinius Superbus, of which two were burnt by herself while the third perished by fire with the Capitol in the days of Sylla. In addition to these facts, Mucianus who was three times consul has stated that he had recently read, while governor of Lycia, a letter written from Troy by Sarpedon; a thing that surprises me the more, if it really was the fact that even in the time of Homer the country that we call Egypt was not in existence. And why too, if paper was then in use, was it the custom, as it is very well known it was, to write upon leaden tablets and linen cloths?

THE DOCTOR

Quacks

Medicine is the only one of the arts of Greece, that, lucrative as it is, the Roman gravity has refused to cultivate. Very few of our fellow citizens have even attempted it, and so soon as they have done so, they have become deserters to the Greeks. Even more than this, if they attempt to treat of it in any other language than Greek they are sure to lose all credit, even with the most ignorant and those who do not understand a word of Greek; there being all the less confidence felt by our people in that which so nearly concerns their welfare, if it happens to be intelligible to them. In fact this is the only one of all the arts, by Hercules! in which the moment a man declares himself to be an adept he is at once believed, there being at the same time no imposture, the results of which are more fraught with peril. To all this we give no attention, so seductive is the sweet influence of the hope entertained of his ultimate recovery by each.

And then besides there is no law in existence to punish the ignorance of physicians, no instance before us of capital punishment inflicted. It is at the expense of our perils that they learn, and they experimentalize by putting us to death, a physician being the only person that can kill another with impunity. Nay, all the blame is thrown upon the sick man only; he is accused of disobedience forthwith and it is the person who is dead and gone that is put upon his trial. It is the usage at Rome for the decuries to pass examination under the censorship of the emperor, and for inquisitions to be made of our party walls: persons who are to sit in judgment on our monetary matters are sent for to the very Pillars of Hercules; while a question of exile is never entertained without a panel of forty-five men selected for the purpose. But when it is the judge's own life that is at stake, who are the persons that are to hold council upon it but those who the very next moment are about to take it!

What profession has there been more fruitful in poisonings or from which there have emanated more frauds upon wills? And then, too, what adulteries have been committed, in the very houses of our princes! the intrigue of Eudemus, for example, with Livia the wife of Drusus Cæsar, and that of Valens with the royal lady. Let us not impute these evils to the art but to the men who practice it.

Colic

Colic is most effectually cured by taking a roasted lark with the food. Some recommend that it should be burnt to ashes in a new vessel, feathers and all, and then pounded and taken for four consecutive days in doses of three spoonfuls in water. Some say that the heart of this bird should be attached to the thigh and, according to others, the heart should be swallowed fresh, quite warm. There is a family of consular dignity known as the Asprenates, two members of which were cured of colic; the one by eating a lark and wearing its heart in a golden bracelet; the other by performing a certain sacrifice in a chapel built of raw bricks in form of a furnace, and then blocking up the edifice the moment the sacrifice was concluded. The ossifrage has a single intestine only, which has the marvelous property of digesting all that the bird has swallowed: the extremity of this intestine, worn as an amulet, is an excellent remedy for colic.

There are certain concealed maladies incident to the intestines, in relation to which there are some marvelous statements made. If to the stomach and chest blind puppies are applied, and suckled with milk from the patient's mouth, the virulence of the malady, it is said, will be transferred to them and in the end they will die: on opening them, the causes of the malady will be sure to be discovered. In all such cases the puppies must be allowed to die, and must be buried in the earth. According to what the magicians say, if the abdomen is touched with a bat's blood the person will be proof against colic for a whole year: when a patient is attacked with the pains of colic, if he can bring himself to drink the water in which he has washed his feet, he will experience a cure.

Asthma

Earthworms are recommended, taken in ordinary wine or raisin wine, or else boiled snails prepared the same way as for the cure of asthma. For the cure of urinary obstructions snails are taken from the shells, pounded, and administered in one cyathus of wine, three the first day, two the second, and one the third. For the expulsion of calculi the empty shells are reduced to ashes and taken in drink: the liver also of a water snake and the ashes of burnt scorpions are similarly employed or are taken with bread or eaten with a locust. For the same purpose the small grits that are found in the gizzard of poultry or in the craw of the ringdove are beaten up and sprinkled in the patient's drink; the craw, too, of poultry is taken, dried, or if fresh, grilled.

For urinary calculi and other obstructions of the bladder, dung of ringdoves is taken with beans; ashes also of wild ringdoves' feathers mixed with vinegar and honey; the intestines of those birds, reduced to ashes and administered in doses of three spoonfuls; a small clod from a swallow's nest dissolved in warm water; the dried crop of an ossifrage; the dung of a turtledove boiled in honied wine; or the broth of a boiled turtledove.

It is very beneficial also for urinary affections to eat thrushes with myrtle berries or grasshoppers grilled on a shallow pan; or else to take the millepedes known as "onisci," in drink. For pains in the bladder a decoction of lambs' feet is used.

Cancer

Ulcers upon the legs and thighs are cured by an application of bears' grease mixed with red earth: and those of a serpiginous nature by using wild boar's gall with resin and white lead; the jawbone of a wild boar or swine reduced to ashes; swine's dung in a dry state; or goats' dung made lukewarm in vinegar. For other kinds of ulcers butter is used as a detergent, and as tending to make new flesh, ashes of deer's antlers or deer's marrow; or else bull's gall mixed with oil of cyprus or oil of iris. Wounds inflicted with edged weapons are rubbed with fresh swine's dung or with dried swine's dung powdered. When ulcers are phagedænic or fistulous bull's gall is injected, with leek juice or woman's milk; or else bull's blood, dried and powdered, with the plant cotyledon.

Carcinomatous sores are treated with hare's rennet, sprinkled upon them with an equal proportion of capers in wine; gangrenes, with bears' grease applied with a feather; and ulcers of a serpiginous nature with the ashes of an ass's hoofs, powdered upon them. The blood of the horse corrodes the flesh by virtue of certain septic powers which it possesses; dried horse dung, too, reduced to ashes has a similar effect. Those kinds of ulcers which are commonly known as "phagedænic" are treated with the ashes of a cow's hide mixed with honey. Calves' flesh, as also cow dung mixed with honey, prevents recent wounds from swelling. The ashes of a leg of veal applied with woman's milk are a cure for sordid ulcers, and the malignant sore known as "cacoëthes"; bull glue, melted, is applied to recent wounds inflicted with edged weapons, the application being removed before the end of three days. Dried goats' milk cheese applied with vinegar and honey acts as a detergent upon ulcers; and goat suet used in combination with wax arrests the spread of serpiginous sores: if employed with pitch and sulphur it will effect a thorough cure. The ashes of a kid's leg, applied with woman's milk, have a similar effect upon malignant ulcers; for the cure of carbuncles a sow's brains are roasted and applied.

The Itch

The itch in man is cured very effectually by using the marrow of an ass or the urine of that animal applied with the mud it has formed upon the ground. Butter, too, is very good, as also in the case of beasts of burden, if applied with warmed resin: bull glue is also used, melted in vinegar and incorporated with lime; or goat's gall mixed with calcined alum. The eruption called "boa," is treated with cow dung, a fact to which it is indebted for its name. The itch in dogs is cured by an application of fresh cows' blood, which, when quite dry is renewed a second time and is rubbed off the next day with strong lie ashes.

Epilepsy

In cases of epilepsy it is a good plan to eat a bear's testes, or those of a wild boar, with mares' milk or water; or else to drink a wild boar's urine with honey and vinegar, that being the best which has been left to dry in the bladder. The testes of swine are prescribed, dried and beaten up in sows' milk, the patient abstaining from wine some days before and after taking the mixture. The lights of a hare are recommended, salted, and taken with one third of frankincense for thirty consecutive days in white wine: hare's rennet also; and asses' brains smoked with burning leaves and administered in hydromel in doses of half an ounce per day.

An ass's hoofs are reduced to ashes and taken for a month together, in doses of two spoonfuls; the testes also of an ass, salted and mixed with the drink, asses' milk or water in particular. The secundines of a she-ass are recommended, more particularly when it is a male that has been foaled: placed beneath the nostrils of the patient when the fits are likely to come on, this substance will effectually repel them.

There are some persons who recommend the patient to eat the heart of a black he-ass in the open air with bread upon the first or second day of the moon: others prescribe the flesh of that animal, and others the blood, diluted with vinegar and taken for forty days together. Some mix horse-stale for this purpose with smithy water fresh from the forge, employing the same mixture for the cure of delirium. Epilepsy is also treated with mares' milk or the excrescences from a horse's legs, taken in honey and vinegar. The magicians highly recommend goats' flesh grilled upon a funeral pile; as also the suet of that animal boiled with an equal quantity of bull's gall and kept in the gall bladder; care being taken not to let it touch the ground, and the patient swallowing it in water, standing aloft. The smell arising from a goat's horns or deer's antlers, burnt, efficiently detects the presence of epilepsy.

Jaundice

For the cure of jaundice, the ashes of a stag's antlers are employed; or the blood of an ass's foal, taken in wine. The first dung that has been voided by the foal after its birth, taken in wine in pieces the size of a bean, will effect a cure by the end of three days. The dung of a newborn colt is possessed of a similar efficacy.

Fevers

Agaric taken in warm water alleviates cold fevers; sideritis in combination with oil is good for tertian fevers; bruised ladanum also, which is found in corn fields; plantago taken in doses of two drachmæ in hydromel, a couple of hours before the paroxysms come on; juice of the root of plantago made warm or subjected to pressure; or else the root itself beaten up in water made warm with a hot iron. Some medical men prescribe three roots of plantago in three cyathi of water; and in a similar manner, four roots for quartan fevers. When buglossos is beginning to wither, if a person takes the pith out of the stem and says while so doing that it is for the cure of such and such a person suffering from fever, and then attaches seven leaves to the patient just before the paroxysms come on he will experience a cure, they say.

Fevers too, those which are attended with recurrent cold shiverings more particularly, are cured by administering one drachma of betony or else agaric in three cyathi of hydromel. Some medical men recommend three leaves of cinquefoil for tertian, four for quartan, and an increased number for other fevers; while others again prescribe in all cases three oboli of cinquefoil, with pepper, in hydromel.

Vervain administered in water is curative of fever in beasts of burden but care must be taken, in cases of tertian fever, to cut the plant at the third joint, and of quartan fever at the fourth. The seed of either kind of hypericon is taken also for quartan fevers and cold shiverings. Powdered betony modifies these fits, and panaces is of so warming a nature that persons when about to travel amid the snow are recommended to drink an infusion of it and to rub the body all over with the plant. Aristolochia also arrests shivering produced by cold.

Leprosy

The buprestis is an insect but rarely found in Italy, and very similar to a scarabæus, with long legs. Concealed among the grass it is very liable to be swallowed unobserved, by oxen in particular; and the moment it comes in contact with the gall it causes such a degree of inflammation that the animal bursts asunder; a circumstance to which the insect owes its name. Applied with he-goat suet it removes lichens on the face, owing to its corrosive properties. A vulture's blood beaten up with cedar resin and root of white chamæleon and covered with a cabbage leaf, when applied is good for the cure of leprosy; the same, too, with the legs of locusts beaten up with he-goat suet. Pimples are treated with poultry grease beaten up and kneaded with onions. One very useful substance for the face is honey in which the bees have died; but a sovereign detergent for that part is swans' grease which has also the property of effacing wrinkles. Brand marks are removed by using pigeons' dung, diluted in vinegar.

The Throat

I find it stated that catarrhs oppressive to the head may be cured by the patient kissing a mule's nostrils. Affections of the uvula and pains in the fauces are alleviated by using the dung of lambs before they have begun to graze, dried in the shade. Diseases of the uvula are cured with the juices of a snail pierced with a needle; the snail, however, must be then hung up in the smoke. The same maladies are treated with ashes of burnt swallows, mixed with honey; a preparation which is equally good for affections of the tonsillary glands. Sheep's milk, used as a gargle, alleviates diseases of the fauces and tonsillary glands.

Millepedes bruised with pigeons' dung are taken as a gargle, with raisin wine; and they are applied externally with dried figs and niter for the purpose of soothing roughness of the fauces and catarrhs. For such cases, too, snails should be boiled unwashed, the earth only being removed, and then pounded and administered to the patient in raisin wine. Some persons are of opinion that for these purposes the snails of Astypalæa are the most efficacious, and they give the preference to the detersive preparation made from them. The parts affected are sometimes rubbed with a cricket, and affections of the tonsillary glands are alleviated by being rubbed with the hands of a person who has bruised a cricket.

Quinsy

For quinsy we have very expeditious remedies in goose gall, mixed with elaterium and honey, an owlet's brains, or the ashes of a burnt swallow, taken in warm water; which last remedy we owe to the poet Ovid. But of all the remedies spoken of as furnished by the swallow, one of the most efficacious is that derived from the young of the wild swallow, a bird which may be easily recognized by the peculiar conformation of its nest. By far the most effectual of them all are the young of the bank swallow, that being the name given to the kind which builds its nest in holes on the banks of rivers. Many persons recommend the young of any kind of swallow as a food, assuring us that the person who takes it need be in no apprehension of quinsy for the whole of the ensuing year. The young of this bird are sometimes stifled and then burnt in a vessel with the blood, the ashes being administered to the patient with bread or in drink: some, however, mix with them the ashes of a burnt weasel in equal proportion. The same remedies are recommended also for scrofula, and they are administered for epilepsy, once a day, in drink. Swallows preserved in salt are taken for quinsy, in doses of one drachma, in drink: the nest of the bird, taken internally, is said to be a cure for the same disease.

Millepedes, it is thought, used in the form of a liniment are peculiarly efficacious for quinsy: some persons administer eleven of them, bruised in one semi-sextarius of hydromel, through a reed, they being of no use whatever if once touched by the teeth.

Opium

The black poppy acts as a soporific, by the juice which exudes from incisions made in the stalk—at the time when the plant is beginning to flower, Diagoras says; but when the blossom has gone off, according to Iollas. This is done at the third hour in a clear, still, day, or when the dew has thoroughly dried upon the poppy. It is recommended to make the incision just beneath the head and calyx of the plant; this being the only kind into the head of which the incision is made. This juice, like that of any other plant, is received in wool; or else, if it is in very minute quantities, it is scraped off with the thumb nail just as it is from the lettuce, and so again on the following day, with the portion that has since dried there. If obtained from the poppy in sufficiently large quantities, this juice thickens, after which it is kneaded out into lozenges and dried in the shade. This juice is possessed not only of certain soporific qualities, but if taken in too large quantities is productive of sleep unto death: the name given to it is "opium." It was in this way, we learn, that the father of P. Licinius Cæcina, a man of Prætorian rank, put an end to his life at Bavilum in Spain, an incurable malady having rendered existence quite intolerable to him. Many other persons have ended their lives in a similar way. It is for this reason that opium has been so strongly exclaimed against by Diagoras and Erasistratus; for they have altogether condemned it as a deadly poison, forbidding it to be used for infusions even, as being injurious to the sight. Andreas says in addition to this that the only reason why it does not cause instantaneous blindness is the fact that they adulterate it at Alexandria. In later times, however, the use of it has not been disapproved of—witness the celebrated preparation known as "diacodion." Lozenges are also made of ground poppy seed, which are taken in milk as a soporific. The seed is employed, too, with rose oil for headache; and in combination with that oil is injected into the ears for earache. Mixed with woman's milk, this seed is used as a liniment for gout: the leaves, too, are employed in a similar manner. Taken in vinegar, the seed is prescribed as a cure for erysipelas and wounds.

The Heart

It is a well-ascertained fact that in the cardiac disease the only resource is wine. According to some authorities wine should only be given when the attacks come on, while others are of opinion that it must only be administered between the attacks; it being the object with the former to arrest the profuse perspirations, while the latter base their practice on an impression that it may be given with more safety at a moment when the malady has diminished in intensity; and this I find is the opinion entertained by most people. In all cases, wine must only be administered just after taking food, never after sleep, and under no circumstances after any other kind of drink, or in other words only when the patient is thirsty; in no case whatever should it be given except at the very last extremity. Wine is better suited to males than to females, to aged people than to youths, to youths than to children, and to persons who are used to it than to those who are not in the habit of taking it; winter, too, is a better time for using it than summer. As to the quantity to be prescribed and the proportion of water to be mixed with it, that depends entirely upon the strength of the wine.

Section XI
ANIMAL FARM

Elephants

Elephants were seen in Italy for the first time in the war with King Pyrrhus, in the year of the City 472; they were called "Lucanian oxen" because they were first seen in Lucania. Seven years after this period they appeared at Rome in a triumph. In the year 502 a great number of them were brought to Rome which had been taken by the pontiff Metellus in his victory gained in Sicily over the Carthaginians; they were one hundred and forty-two in number or, as some say, one hundred and forty, and were conveyed to our shores upon rafts which were constructed on rows of hogsheads joined together. Verrius informs us that they fought in the Circus and that they were slain with javelins, for want of some better method of disposing of them; as the people neither liked to keep them nor yet to give them to the kings. L. Piso tells us only that they were brought into the Circus; and for the purpose of increasing the feeling of contempt towards them they were driven all round the area of that place by workmen who had nothing but spears blunted at the point. The authors who are of opinion that they were not killed do not, however, inform us how they were afterwards disposed of.

There is a famous combat mentioned of a Roman with an elephant, when Hannibal compelled our prisoners to fight against each other. The one who had survived all the others he placed before an elephant and promised him his life if he should slay it; upon which the man advanced alone into the arena and, to the great regret of the Carthaginians, succeeded in doing so. Hannibal, thinking that the news of this victory might cause a feeling of contempt for these animals, sent some horsemen to kill the man on

97

his way home. In our battles with Pyrrhus it was found, on making trial, that it was extremely easy to cut off the trunks of these animals. Fenestella informs us that they fought at Rome in the Circus for the first time during the curule ædileship of Claudius Pulcher, in the consulship of M. Antonius and A. Postumius, in the year of the City 655; and that twenty years afterwards, during the curule ædileship of the Luculli, they were set to fight against bulls. In the second consulship of Pompeius, at the dedication of the temple of Venus Victrix, twenty elephants or, as some say, seventeen, fought in the Circus against a number of Gætulians who attacked them with javelins. One of these animals fought in a most astonishing manner; being pierced through the feet, it dragged itself on its knees towards the troop, and seizing their bucklers tossed them aloft into the air: and as they came to the ground they greatly amused the spectators for they whirled round and round in the air just as if they had been thrown up with a certain degree of skill and not by the frantic fury of a wild beast. Another very wonderful circumstance happened; an elephant was killed by a single blow. The weapon pierced the animal below the eye and entered the vital part of the head. The elephants attempted by their united efforts to break down the enclosure, not without great confusion among the people who surrounded the iron gratings. It was in consequence of this circumstance that Cæsar the Dictator, when he was afterwards about to exhibit a similar spectacle, had the arena surrounded with trenches of water, which were lately filled up by the Emperor Nero when he added the seats for the equestrian order. When the elephants in the exhibition given by Pompeius had lost all hopes of escaping they implored the compassion of the multitude by attitudes which surpass all description, and with a kind of lamentation bewailed their unhappy fate. So greatly were the people affected by the scene that, forgetting the general altogether, and the munificence which had been at such pains to do them honor, the whole assembly rose up in tears and showered curses on Pompeius, of which he soon afterwards became the victim. They fought also in the third consulship of the Dictator Cæsar, twenty of them against five hundred foot soldiers. On another occasion twenty elephants, carrying towers, and each defended by sixty men, were opposed to the same number of foot soldiers as before, and an equal number of horsemen. Afterwards under the Emperors Claudius and Nero the last exploit that the gladiators performed was fighting singlehanded with elephants.

The first harnessed elephants that were seen at Rome were in the triumph of Pompeius Magnus over Africa, when they drew his chariot; a thing that is said to have been done long before at the triumph of Father Liber on the conquest of India. Procilius says that those which were used at the triumph of Pompeius were unable to go in harness through the gate of the city. In the exhibition of gladiators which was given by Germanicus the elephants performed a sort of dance with their uncouth and irregular movements. It was a common thing to see them throw arrows with such strength that the wind was unable to turn them from their course, to imitate among themselves the combats of the gladiators, and to frolic through the steps of the Pyrrhic dance. After this they walked upon the tightrope, and four of them would carry a litter in which lay a fifth which represented a woman lying-in. They afterwards took their places at table, reclining upon couches which were filled with people; and so nicely did they manage their steps that they did not so much as touch any of those who were drinking there.

It is a well-known fact that one of these animals who was slower than usual in learning what was taught him and had been frequently chastised with blows was found conning over his lesson in the nighttime. It is a most surprising thing also that the elephant is able not only to walk up the tightrope backwards; but to come down it as well with the head foremost. Mutianus, who was three times consul, informs us that one of these animals had been taught to trace the Greek letters and that he used to write in that language the following words: "I have myself written these words, and have dedicated the Celtic spoils." Mutianus states also that he himself was witness to the fact that when some elephants were being landed at Puteoli and were compelled to leave the ship, being terrified at the length of the platform which extended from the vessel to the shore, they walked backwards in order to deceive themselves by forming a false estimate of the distance.

The Mice of Pontus

The mice of Pontus conceal themselves during the winter; but only the white ones. I wonder how those authors who have asserted that the sense of taste in these animals is very acute found out that such is the fact. The Alpine mice which are the same size as badgers also conceal themselves; but they first carry a store of provisions into their retreat. Some writers say that the male and female, lying on their backs alternately, hold in their paws a bundle of gnawed herbs, and the tail of each in its turn being seized by the teeth of the other, in this way, they are dragged into their hole; hence it is, that at this season their hair is found to be rubbed off their backs. There is a similar animal also in Egypt, which sits in the same way upon its haunches and walks on two feet, using the forefeet as hands.

Hedgehogs

Hedgehogs also lay up food for the winter; rolling themselves on apples as they lie on the ground they pierce one with their quills and then take up another in the mouth and so carry them into the hollows of trees. These

animals, when they conceal themselves in their holes, afford
a sure sign that the wind is about to change from northeast
to south.

Bears

The head of the bear is extremely weak, whereas
in the lion it is remarkable for its strength: on which account it is that when the bear, impelled by any alarm, is
about to precipitate itself from a rock it covers its head with
its paws. In the arena of the Circus they are often to be
seen killed by a blow on the head with the fist. The people of Spain have a belief that there is some kind of magi-
cal poison in the brain of the bear, and therefore burn the
heads of those that have been killed in their public games;
for it is averred that the brain, when mixed with drink, produces in man the rage of the bear. These animals walk on
two feet and climb down trees backwards. They can overcome the bull by suspending themselves by all four legs
from its muzzle and horns, thus wearing out its powers by
their weight. In no other animal is stupidity found more
adroit in devising mischief. It is recorded in our Annals
that on the fourteenth day before the calends of October
in the consulship of M. Piso and M. Messala, Domitus
Ahenobarbus the curule ædile brought into the Circus
one hundred Numidian bears, and as many Æthiopian hunters. I am surprised to find the word Numidian added, seeing that it is well known that there are no bears produced
in Africa.

Dogs

A dog to which Darius gives the name of Hyr-
canus, upon the funeral pile of King Lysimachus being
lighted, threw itself into the flames, and the dog of King

Hiero did the same. Philistus also gives a similar account of Pyrrhus, the dog of the tyrant Gelon: and it is said that the dog of Nicomedes, king of Bithynia, tore Consingis, the wife of that king, in consequence of her wanton behavior when toying with her husband.

Among ourselves Volcatius, a man of rank who instructed Cascellius in the civil law, as he was riding on his Asturian jennet towards evening from his country-house was attacked by a robber and was only saved by his dog. The senator Cælius while lying sick at Placentia was surprised by armed men, but received not a wound from them until they had first killed his dog. But a more extraordinary fact than all is what took place in our own times and is testified by the public register of the Roman people. In the consulship of Appius Junius and P. Silius, when Titius Sabinus was put to death, together with his slaves, for the affair of Nero the son of Germanicus, it was found impossible to drive away a dog which belonged to one of them from the prison; nor could it be forced away from the body, which had been cast down the Gemitorian steps; but there it stood howling, in the presence of vast multitudes of people; and when some one threw a piece of bread to it the animal carried it to the mouth of its master. Afterwards, when the body was thrown into the Tiber, the dog swam into the river, and endeavored to raise it out of the water; quite a throng of people collected to witness this instance of an animal's fidelity.

Dogs are the only animals that are sure to know their master; and if they suddenly meet him as a stranger they will instantly recognize him. They are the only animals that will answer to their names, and recognize the voices of the family. They recollect a road along which they have passed, however long it may be. Next to man, there is no living creature whose memory is so retentive. By sitting down on the ground we may arrest their most impetuous attack, even when prompted by the most violent rage.

In daily life we have discovered many other valuable

qualities in this animal; but its intelligence and sagacity are more especially shown in the chase. It discovers and traces out the tracks of the animal, leading by the leash the sportsman who accompanies it straight up to the prey; and as soon as ever it has perceived it, how silent it is, and how secret but significant is the indication which it gives, first by the tail and afterwards by the nose! Hence it is that even when worn out with old age, blind, and feeble, they are carried by the huntsman in his arms, being still able to point out the coverts where the game is concealed, by snuffing with their muzzles at the wind.

Horses

Those who have to use the javelin are well aware how the horse, by its exertions and the supple movements of its body, aids the rider in any difficulty he may have in throwing his weapon. They will even present to their master the weapons collected on the ground. The horses too that are yoked to the chariots in the Circus, beyond a doubt display remarkable proofs how sensible they are to encouragement and to glory. In the Secular games which were celebrated in the Circus under the Emperor Claudius, when the charioteer Corax who belonged to the white party was thrown from his place at the starting-post, his horses took the lead and kept it, opposing the other chariots, overturning them, and doing every thing against the other competitors that could have been done had they been guided by the most skillful charioteer; and while we quite blushed to behold the skill of man excelled by that of the horse, they arrived at the goal after going over the whole of the prescribed course. Our ancestors considered it as a still more remarkable portent that when a charioteer had been thrown from his place in the plebeian games of the Circus, the horses ran to the Capitol, just as if he had been standing in the car, and went three times round the temple there. But what is the greatest prodigy of all is the fact that the horses of Ratumenna came from Veii to Rome with the palm branch and chaplet, he himself having fallen from his chariot after having gained the victory; from which circumstance the Ratumennian gate derived its name.

When the Sarmatæ are about to undertake a long journey they prepare their horses for it by making them fast the day before, during which they give them but little to drink; by these means they are enabled to travel on horseback, without stopping, for one hundred and fifty miles. Some horses are known to live fifty years; but the females are not so long-lived. These last come to their full growth at the fifth year, the males a year later. The points requisite for the Circus are somewhat different and while horses are put in training for other purposes at only two years old, they are not admitted to the contests of the Circus before their fifth year.

Bulls

The bull has a proud air, a stern forehead, shaggy ears, and horns which appear always ready and challenging to the combat; but it is by his forefeet that he manifests his threatening anger. As his rage increases, he stands lashing back his tail every now and then, and throwing up the sand against his belly; being the only animal that excites himself by these means. We have seen them fight at the word of command, and shown as a public spectacle; these bulls whirled about and then fell upon their horns, and at once were up again; then at other times they would lie upon the ground and let themselves be lifted up; they would even stand in a two-horsed chariot while moving at a rapid rate, like so many charioteers. The people of Thessaly invented a method of killing bulls by means of a man on horseback who would ride up to them and seize one of the horns, and so twist their neck. Cæsar the Dictator was the first person who exhibited this spectacle at Rome.

Bulls are selected as the very choicest of victims and are offered up as the most approved sacrifice for appeasing the gods. Of all the animals that have long tails this is the only one whose tail is not of proportionate length at the moment of birth; and in this animal alone it continues to grow until it reaches its heels. It is on this account that in making choice of a calf for a victim due care is taken that its tail reaches to the pastern joint; if it is shorter than this the sacrifice is not deemed acceptable to the gods. This fact has also been remarked, that calves which have been carried to the altar on men's shoulders are not generally acceptable to the gods; and also, if they are lame or of a species which is not appropriate, or if they struggle to get away from the altar. It was a not uncommon prodigy among the ancient for an ox to speak; upon such a fact being announced to the senate they were in the habit of holding a meeting in the open air.

In Egypt an ox is even worshipped as a deity; they call it Apis. It is distinguished by a conspicuous white spot on the right side, in the form of a crescent. There is a knot also under the tongue which is called "cantharus." This ox is not allowed to live beyond a certain number of years; it is then destroyed by being drowned in the fountain of the priests. They then go, amid general mourning, and seek another ox to replace it; and the mourning is continued, with their heads shaved, until such time as they have found one; it is not long, however, at any time before they meet with a successor. When one has been found it is brought by the priests to Memphis. There are two temples appropriated to it which are called thalami, and to these the people resort to learn the auguries. According as the ox enters the one or the other of these places the augury is deemed favorable or unfavorable. It gives answers to individuals by taking food from the hand of those who consult it. It turned away from the hand of Germanicus Cæsar, and not long after he died. In general it lives in secret; but, when it comes forth in public the multitudes make way for it and it is attended by a crowd of boys singing hymns in honor of it; it appears to be sensible of the adoration thus paid to it, and to court it. These crowds, too, suddenly become inspired and predict future events.

Apes

The different kinds of apes which approach the nearest to the human figure are distinguished from each other by the tail. Their shrewdness is quite wonderful. It is said that, imitating the hunters, they will besmear themselves with bird lime and put their feet into the shoes which, as snares, have been prepared for them. Mucianus says that they have even played at chess, having by practice learned to distinguish the different pieces, which are made of wax. He says that the species which have tails become quite melancholy when the moon is on the wane, and that they leap for joy at the time of the new moon and adore it. Other quadrupeds also are terrified at the eclipses of the heavenly bodies. All the species of apes manifest remarkable affection for their offspring. Females which have been domesticated and have had young ones carry them about and show them to all comers, show great delight when they are caressed, and appear to understand the kindness thus shown them. Hence it is that they very often stifle their young with their embraces. The dog's-headed ape is of a much fiercer nature, as is the case with the satyr. The callitriche has almost a totally different aspect; it has a beard on the face, and a tail, which in the first part of it is very bushy. It is said that this animal cannot live except in the climate of Æthiopia, which is its native place.

Crocodiles

The skin of the belly of the crocodile is soft and thin; aware of this, the dolphins plunge into the water as if in great alarm, and diving beneath its belly, tear it open with their spines. There is a race of men also who are peculiarly hostile to this animal; they are known as the Tentyritæ, from an island in the Nile which they inhabit. These men are of small stature but of wonderful presence of mind, though for this particular object only. The crocodile is a terrible animal to those who fly from it, while at the same time it will fly from those who pursue it; these, however, are the only people who dare to attack it. They even swim in the river after it and mount its back like so many horsemen; and just as the animal turns up its head for the purpose of biting them they insert a club into its mouth, holding which at each end with the two hands, it acts like a bit, and by these means they drive the captured animal on shore. They also terrify the crocodile so much by their voice as to force it to disgorge the bodies which it has lately swallowed, for the purpose of burial. This island, therefore, is the only place near which the crocodile never swims; indeed it is repelled by the odor of this race of men. The sight of this animal is said to be dull when it is in the water, but when out of the water, piercing in the extreme; it always passes the four winter months in a cave without taking food. Some persons say that this is the only animal that continues to increase in size as long as it lives; it is very longlived.

The Hippopotamus

The Nile produces the hippopotamus, another wild beast, of a still greater size. It has the cloven hoof of the ox; the back, the mane, and the neighing of the horse; and the turned-up snout, the tail and the hooked teeth of the wild boar, but not so dangerous. The hide is impenetrable, except when it has been soaked with water; and it is used for making shields and helmets. This animal lays waste the standing corn and determines beforehand what part it shall ravage on the following day; it is said also that it enters the field backwards to prevent any ambush being laid for it on its return.

M. Scaurus was the first who exhibited this animal at Rome, together with five crocodiles, at the games which he gave in his ædileship, in a piece of water which had been temporarily prepared for the purpose.

Lions

When the lioness is defending her whelps, it is said that she fixes her eyes steadily on the ground, that she may not be frightened at the spears of the hunters. In all other respects these animals are equally free from deceit and suspicion. They never look at an object obliquely and they dislike being looked at themselves in such a manner. It is generally believed that when the lion is dying he bites at the earth and sheds tears at his fate. Powerful and fierce as this animal is, he is terrified by the motion of wheels or of an empty chariot, and still more on seeing the crest or hearing the crowing of a cock; but most of all is he afraid of fire. The only malady to which the lion is subject is loss of appetite; this, however, is cured by putting insults upon him by means of the pranks of monkeys placed about him, a thing which rouses his anger; immediately he tastes their blood he is relieved.

Q. Scævola the son of P. Scævola when he was curule ædile was the first to exhibit at Rome a combat of a number of lions; and L. Sylla, who was afterwards Dictator, during his prætorship gave the spectacle of a fight of one hundred lions with manes. After him, Pompeius Magnus exhibited six hundred lions in the Circus, three hundred and fifteen of which had manes: Cæsar the Dictator exhibited four hundred.

It was formerly a very difficult matter to catch the lion, and it was mostly done by means of pitfalls. In the reign of the Emperor Claudius, accident disclosed a method which appears almost disgraceful to the name of such an animal; a Gætulian shepherd stopped a lion that was rushing furiously upon him by merely throwing his cloak over the animal; a circumstance which afterwards afforded an exhibition in the arena of the Circus when the frantic fury of the animal was paralyzed in a manner almost incredible by a light covering being thrown over its head, so much so that it was put into chains without the least resistance; we must conclude, therefore, that all its strength lies in its eyes. This circumstance renders what was done by Lysimachus less wonderful, who strangled a lion with which he had been shut up by command of Alexander.

Antony subjected lions to the yoke, and was the first at Rome to harness them to his chariot.

Panthers and Tigers

The panther and the tiger are nearly the only animals that are remarkable for a skin distinguished by the variety of its spots; whereas others have them of a single color appropriate to each species. The lions of Syria alone are black. The spots of the panther are like small eyes upon a white ground. It is said that all quadrupeds are attracted in a most wonderful manner by their odor, while they are terrified by the fierceness of their aspect; for which reason the creature conceals its head and then seizes upon the animals that are attracted to it by the sweetness of the odor. It is said by some that the panther has on the shoulder a spot which bears the form of the moon;

and that like it, it regularly increases to full, and then diminishes to a crescent. At present we apply the general names of varia and pard, which last belongs to the males, to all the numerous species of this animal which is very common in Africa and Syria. Some writers distinguish the panther as being remarkable for its whiteness: but as yet I have not observed any other difference between them.

There was an ancient decree of the senate which prohibited animals being imported from Africa into Italy; but Cn. Aufidius the tribune of the people procured a law repealing this, which allowed of their being brought over for the games of the Circus. Scaurus in his ædileship was the first who sent over the parti-colored kind, one hundred and fifty in the whole; after which, Pompeius Magnus sent four hundred and ten, and the late Emperor Augustus four hundred and twenty.

The same emperor was the first person who exhibited at Rome a tame tiger on the stage. This was in the consulship of Q. Tubero and Fabius Maximus at the dedication of the theater of Marcellus on the fourth day before the nones of May: the late Emperor Claudius exhibited four at one time.

Section XII
BIRDS

The Nightingale

The song of the nightingale is to be heard without intermission for fifteen days and nights continuously when the foliage is thickening, as it bursts from the bud; a bird which deserves our admiration in no slight degree. First of all, what a powerful voice in so small a body! its note, how long and how well sustained! And then, too, it is the only bird the notes of which are modulated in accordance with the strict rules of musical science. At one moment, as it sustains its breath, it will prolong its note, and then at another will vary it with different inflexions; then again it will break into distinct chirrups or pour forth an endless series of roulades. Then it will warble to itself while taking breath, or else disguise its voice in an instant; while sometimes it will twitter to itself, now with a full note, now with a grave, now again sharp, now with a broken note and now with a prolonged one. Sometimes when it thinks fit it . will break out into quavers, and will run through in succession, alto, tenor, and bass: in a word, in so tiny a throat is to be found all the melody that the ingenuity of man has ever discovered through the medium of the invention of the most exquisite flute: so much so that there can be no doubt it was an infallible presage of his future sweetness as a poet when one of these creatures perched and sang on the infant lips of the poet Stesichorus.

That there may remain no doubt that there is a certain degree of art in its performances, we may here remark that every bird has a number of notes peculiar to itself; for they do not all of them have the same, but each certain melodies of its own. They vie with one another, and the spirit with which they contend is evident to all. The one that is vanquished often dies in the contest and will rather yield its life than its song. The younger birds are listening in the meantime and receive the lesson in song from which they are to profit. The learner hearkens with the greatest attention and repeats what it has heard, and then they are silent by turns; this is understood to be the correction of an error on the part of the scholar and a sort of reproof, as it were, on the part of the teacher. Hence it is that nightingales fetch as high a price as slaves, and indeed sometimes more than used formerly to be paid for a man in a suit of armor.

I know that on one occasion six thousand sesterces were paid for a nightingale, a white one it is true, a thing that is hardly ever to be seen, to be made a present to Agrippina, the wife of the Emperor Claudius. A nightingale has been often seen that will sing at command, and take alternate parts with the music that accompanies it.

Pigeons

Next to the partridge, it is in the pigeon that similar tendencies are to be seen; but then chastity is especially observed by it, and promiscuous intercourse is a thing quite unknown. Although inhabiting a domicile in common with others, they will none of them violate the laws of conjugal fidelity: not one will desert its nest unless it is either widower or widow. Although the males are very imperious and sometimes even extremely exacting, the females put up with it: for in fact the males sometimes suspect them of infidelity though by nature they are incapable of it. On such occasions the throat of the male seems quite choked with indignation, and he inflicts severe blows with the beak, then afterwards to make some atonement he falls to billing, and by way of pressing his amorous solicitations, sidles round and round the female with his feet. They both of them manifest an equal degree of affection for their offspring; indeed it is not unfrequently that this is a ground for correction, in consequence of the female being too slow in going to her young. When the female is sitting the male renders her every attention that can in any way tend to her solace and comfort. The first thing that they do is to eject from the throat some saltish earth which they have digested into the mouths of the young ones, in order to prepare them in due time to receive their nutriment. It is a peculiarity of the pigeon and of the turtle-dove not to throw back the neck when drinking, but to take in the water at a long draught just as beasts of burden do.

We read in some authors that the ringdove lives so long as thirty years, and sometimes as much as forty, without any other inconvenience than the extreme length of the claws, which with them, in fact, is the chief mark of old age; they can be cut, however, without any danger. The voice of all these birds is similar, being composed of three notes and then a mournful noise at the end. In winter they are silent and they only recover their voice in the spring. Nigidius expresses it as his opinion that the ring dove will abandon the place if she hears her name mentioned under the roof where she is sitting on her eggs: they hatch their young just after the summer solstice. Pigeons and turtledoves live eight years.

The sparrow on the other hand, which has an equal degree of salaciousness, is shortlived in the extreme. It is said that the male does not live beyond a year; and as a ground for this belief it is stated that at the beginning of spring the black marks are never to be seen upon the beak which began to appear in the summer. The females are said to live somewhat longer.

Pigeons have even a certain appreciation of glory. There is reason for believing that they are well aware of the colors of their plumage and the various shades which it presents, and even in their very mode of flying they court our applause as they cleave the air in every direction. It is indeed through this spirit of ostentation that they are handed over, fast bound as it were, to the hawk; for from the noise that they make by the flapping of their wings, their long feathers become twisted and disordered: otherwise, when they can fly without any impediment, they are far swifter in their movements than the hawk. The robber, lurking amid the dense foliage, keeps on the look-out for them and seizes them at the very moment that they are indulging their vainglorious self-complaisance.

It is for this reason that it is necessary to keep along with the pigeons the bird that is known as the "tinnunculus"; as it protects them, and by its natural superiority scares away the hawk; so much so that the hawk will vanish at the very sight of it, and the instant it hears its voice. Hence it is that the pigeons have an especial regard for this bird; and, it is said if one of these birds is buried at each of the four corners of the pigeon house in pots that have been newly glazed the pigeons will not change their abode—a result which has been obtained by some by cutting a joint of their wings with an instrument of gold; for if any other were used the wounds would be not unattended with danger.

The pigeon in general may be looked upon as a bird fond of change; they have the art among themselves of gaining one another over, and so seducing their companions: hence it is that we frequently find them return attended by others which they have enticed away.

In addition to this, pigeons have acted as messengers in affairs of importance. During the siege of Mutina, Decimus Brutus, who was in the town, sent despatches to the camp of the consuls fastened to pigeons' feet. Of what use to Antony then were his intrenchments and all the vigilance of the besieging army, his nets, too, which he had spread in the river, while the messenger of the besieged was cleaving the air?

Many persons have quite a mania for pigeons—building towns for them on the top of their roofs, and taking a pleasure in relating the pedigree and noble origin of each.

The Peacock

We shall now speak of the second class of birds, which is divided into two kinds; those which give omens by their note, and those which afford presages by their flight. The variation of the note in the one, and the relative size in the other, constitute the differences between them. These last, therefore, shall be treated of first, and the peacock shall have precedence of all the rest, as much for its singular beauty as its superior instinct and the vanity it displays.

When it hears itself praised this bird spreads out its gorgeous colors, and especially if the sun happens to be shining at the time, because then they are seen in all their radiance and to better advantage. At the same time, spreading out its tail in the form of a shell, it throws the reflection upon the other feathers which shine all the more brilliantly when a shadow is cast upon them; then at another moment it will contract all the eyes depicted upon its feathers in a single mass, manifesting great delight in having them admired by the spectator. The peacock loses its tail every year at the fall of the leaf, and a new one shoots forth in its place at the flower season; between these periods the bird is abashed and moping and seeks retired spots. The peacock lives twenty-five years, and begins to show its colors in the third. By some authors it is stated that this bird is not only a vain creature but of a spiteful disposition also, just in the same way that they attribute bashfulness to the goose. The characteristics, however, which they have thus ascribed to these birds appear to me to be utterly unfounded.

The orator Hortensius was the first Roman who

had the peacock killed for table; it was on the occasion of the banquet given by him on his inauguration in the college of the priesthood. M. Aufidius Lurco was the first who taught the art of fattening them, about the time of the last war with the Pirates. From this source of profit he acquired an income of sixty thousand sesterces.

The Dunghill Cock

Next after the peacock, the animal that acts as our watchman by night, and which Nature has produced for the purpose of arousing mortals to their labors and dispelling their slumbers, shows itself most actuated by feelings of vanity. The cock knows how to distinguish the stars and marks the different periods of the day, every three hours, by his note. These animals go to roost with the setting of the sun, and at the fourth watch of the camp recall man to his cares and toils. They do not allow the rising of the sun to creep upon us unawares, but by their note proclaim the coming day, and they prelude their crowing by clapping their sides with their wings. They exercise a rigorous sway over the other birds of their kind, and in every place where they are kept hold the supreme command. This, however, is only obtained after repeated battles among themselves, as they are well aware that they have weapons on their legs, produced for that very purpose, as it were, and the contest often ends in the death of both the combatants at the same moment. If, on the other hand, one of them obtains the mastery he instantly by his note proclaims himself the conqueror and testifies by his crowing that he has been victorious; while his conquered opponent silently slinks away and, though with a very bad grace, submits to servitude. And with equal pride does the throng of the poultry yard strut along with head uplifted and crest erect. These are the only ones among the winged race that repeatedly look up to the heavens, with the tail, which in its drooping shape resembles a sickle, raised aloft: and so it is that these birds inspire terror even in the lion, the most courageous of all animals.

Some of these birds are reared for nothing but warfare and perpetual combats, and have even shed a luster thereby on their native places, Rhodes and Tanagra. The next rank is considered to belong to those of Melos and Chalcis. Hence it is not without very good reason that the consular purple of Rome pays these birds such singular honors. It is from the feeding of these creatures that the omens by fowls are derived; it is these that regulate day by day the movements of our magistrates, and open or shut to them their own houses, as the case may be; it is these that give an impulse to the fasces of the Roman magistracy, or withhold them; it is these that command battles or forbid them, and furnish auspices for victories to be gained in every part of the world. It is these that hold supreme rule over those who are themselves the rulers of the earth, and whose entrails and fibers are as pleasing to the gods as the first spoils of victory. Their note, when heard at an unusual hour or in the evening, has also its peculiar presages; for on one occasion, by crowing the whole night through for several nights, they presaged to the Bœotians that famous victory which they gained over the Lacedæmonians; such in fact being the interpretation that was put upon it by way of prognostic, as this bird, when conquered, is never known to crow.

Those eggs which have been laid within the last ten days are the best for putting under the hen; old ones or those which have just been laid will be unfruitful; an uneven number also ought to be placed. On the fourth day after the hen has begun to sit, if, upon taking an egg with one hand by the two ends and holding it up to the light, it is found to be clear and of one uniform color it is most likely to be barren, and another should be substituted in its place. There is also a way of testing them by means of water; an empty egg will float on the surface while those that fall to the bottom, or in other words, are full, should be placed under the hen. Care must be taken, however, not to make trial by shaking them, for if the organs which are necessary for life become confused, they will come to nothing. Incubation ought to begin just after the new moon; for, if commenced before the eggs will be unproductive. The chickens are hatched sooner if the weather is warm: hence it is that in summer they break the shell on the nineteenth day, but in winter on the twenty-fifth only. If it happens to thunder during the time of incubation, the eggs are addled, and if the cry of a hawk is heard they are spoilt. The best remedy against the effects of thunder is to put an iron nail beneath the straw on which the eggs are laid, or else some earth from off a plough-share. Some eggs, however, are hatched by the spontaneous action of Nature, without the process of incubation, as is the case in the dunghills of Egypt. There is a well-known story related about a man at Syracuse, who was in the habit of covering eggs with earth, and then continuing his drinking bout till they were hatched.

And, what is even more singular still, eggs can be hatched also by a human being. Julia Augusta, when pregnant in her early youth of Tiberius Cæsar, by Nero, was particularly desirous that her offspring should be a son, and accordingly employed the following mode of divination which was then much in use among young women: she carried an egg in her bosom taking care whenever she was obliged to put it down to give it to her nurse to warm in her own, that there might be no interruption in the heat: it is stated that the result promised by this mode of augury was not falsified.

It was perhaps from this circumstance that the modern invention took its rise of placing eggs in a warm spot and covering them with chaff, the heat being maintained by a moderate fire, while in the meantime a man is employed in turning them. By the adoption of this plan, the young, all of them, break the shell on a stated day. There is a story told of a breeder of poultry of such remarkable skill that on seeing an egg he could tell which hen had laid it. It is said also that when a hen has happened to die while sitting the males have been seen to take her place in turns and perform all the other duties of a brood-hen, taking care in the meantime to abstain from crowing. But the most remarkable thing of all is the sight of a hen, beneath which ducks' eggs have been put and hatched. At first she is unable to quite recognize the brood as her own while in her anxiety she gives utterance to her clucking as she doubtfully calls them; then at last she will stand at the margin of the pond uttering her laments while the ducklings with Nature for their guide are diving beneath the water.

The breed of a fowl is judged of by the erectness of the crest which is sometimes double, its black wings, reddish beak, and toes of unequal number, there being sometimes a fifth placed transversely above the other four. For the purposes of divination those that have a yellow beak and feet are not considered pure; while for the secret rites of Bona Dea, black ones are chosen. There is also a dwarf species of fowl which is not barren either; a thing that is the case with no other kind of bird. These dwarfs rarely lay at any stated periods, and their incubation is productive of injury to the eggs.

Swallows

The swallow, the only bird that is carnivorous among those which have not hooked talons, takes its departure also during the winter months; but it only goes to neighboring countries seeking sunny retreats there on the mountainsides; sometimes they have been found in such spots bare and quite unfledged. This bird, it is said, will not enter a house in Thebes because that city has been captured so frequently; nor will it approach the country of the Bizyæ on account of the crimes committed there by Tereus. Cæcina of Volaterræ, a member of the equestrian order and the owner of several chariots, used to have swallows caught and then carried them with him to Rome. Upon gaining a victory he would send the news by them to his friends; for after staining them the color of the party that had gained the day he would let them go, immediately upon which they would make their way to the nests they had previously occupied. Fabius Pictor also relates in his Annals that when a Roman garrison was being besieged by the Ligurians, a swallow which had been taken from its young ones was brought to him in order that he might give them notice by the number of knots on a string tied to its leg, on what day succor would arrive, and a sortie might be made with advantage.

Birds Which Speak

There are some birds that can imitate the human voice, the parrot for instance, which can even converse. India sends us this bird which it calls by the name of "sittaces"; the body is green all over only it is marked with a ring of red around the neck. It will duly salute an emperor and pronounce the words it has heard spoken; it is rendered especially frolicsome under the influence of wine. Its head is as hard as its beak, and this, when it is being taught to talk, is beaten with a rod of iron for otherwise it is quite insensible to blows. When it lights on the ground it falls upon its beak, and by resting upon it makes itself all the lighter for its feet which are naturally weak.

The magpie is much less famous for its talking qualities than the parrot, because it does not come from a distance, and yet it can speak with much more distinctness. These birds love to hear words spoken which they can utter; and not only do they learn them but are pleased at the task; and as they con them over to themselves with the greatest care and attention, make no secret of the interest they feel. It is a well-known fact that a magpie has died before now, when it has found itself mastered by a difficult word that it could not pronounce. Their memory, however, will fail them if they do not from time to time hear the same word repeated; and while they are trying to recollect it they will show the most extravagant joy if they happen to hear it. Their appearance, although there is nothing remarkable in it, is by no means plain; but they have quite sufficient beauty in their singular ability to imitate the human speech.

It is said that it is only the kind of pie which feeds upon acorns that can be taught to speak; and that those which have five toes on each foot can be taught with the greatest facility; but only during the first two years of their life. The magpie has a broader tongue than is usual with most other birds; which is the case also with all the other birds that can imitate the human voice; although some individuals of almost every kind have the faculty of doing so.

Agrippina the wife of Claudius Cæsar had a thrush that could imitate human speech, a thing that was never known before the moment that I am writing this, the young Cæsars have a starling and some nightingales that are being taught to talk in Greek and Latin; besides which they are studying their task the whole day, continually repeating the new words that they have learnt and giving utterance to phrases even of considerable length. Birds are taught to talk in a retired spot and where no other voice can be heard, so as to interfere with their lesson; a person sits by them and continually repeats the words he wishes them to learn, while at the same time he encourages them by giving them food.

Let us do justice also to the raven, whose merits have been attested not only by the sentiments of the Roman people but by the strong expression, also, of their indignation. In the reign of Tiberius one of a brood of ravens that had bred on the top of the temple of Castor happened to fly into a shoemaker's shop that stood opposite: upon which, from a feeling of religious veneration, it was looked upon as doubly recommended by the owner of the place. The bird, having been taught to speak at an early age, used every morning to fly to the Rostra, which look towards the Forum; here, addressing each by his name, it would salute Tiberius and then the Cæsars Germanicus and Drusus, after which it would proceed to greet the Roman populace as they passed and then return to the shop: for several years it was remarkable for the constancy of its attendance. The owner of another shoemaker's shop in the neighborhood, in a sudden fit of anger killed the bird, enraged, as he would have had it appear, because with its ordure it had soiled some shoes of his. Upon this there was such rage manifested by the multitude that he was at once driven from that part of the city and soon after put to death. The funeral of the bird was celebrated with almost endless obsequies; the body was placed upon a litter carried upon the shoulders of two Æthiopians preceded by a piper and borne to the pile with garlands of every size and description.

The Eagle

Caius Marius in his second consulship assigned the eagle exclusively to the Roman legions. Before that period it had only held the first rank, there being four others as well, the wolf, the minotaur, the horse, and the wild boar, each of which preceded a single division. Some few years before his time it had begun to be the custom to carry the eagle only into battle, the other standards being left behind in camp; Marius, however, abolished the rest of them entirely. Since then it has been remarked that hardly ever has a Roman legion encamped for the winter without a pair of eagles making their appearance at the spot.

The first and second species of eagle not only prey

upon the whole of the smaller quadrupeds, but will attack deer. Rolling in the dust, the eagle covers its body all over with it and then perching on the antlers of the animal shakes the dust into its eyes, while at the same time it beats it on the head with its wings until the creature at last precipitates itself down the rocks. Nor is this one enemy sufficient for it; it has still more terrible combats with the dragon, and the issue is much more doubtful although the battle is fought in the air. The dragon seeks the eggs of the eagle with a mischievous avidity; while the eagle in return carries it off whenever it happens to see it; upon these occasions the dragon coils itself about the wings of the bird in multiplied folds until at last they fall to the earth together.

There is a very famous story about an eagle at the city of Sestos. Having been reared by a little girl, it used to testify its gratitude for her kindness, first by bringing her birds, and in due time various kinds of prey: at last she died, upon which the bird threw itself on the lighted pile and was consumed with her body. In memory of this event the inhabitants raised upon the spot what they called an heroic monument in honor of Jupiter and the damsel, the eagle being a bird consecrated to that divinity.

Hawks

In the part of Thrace which lies above Amphipolis men and hawks go in pursuit of prey in a sort of partnership as it were; for while the men drive the birds from out of the woods and the reed beds the hawks bring them down as they fly; and after they have taken the game the fowlers share it with them. It has been said that when sent aloft they will pick out the birds that are wanted, and that when the opportune moment for taking them has come they invite the fowler to seize the opportunity by their cries and their peculiar mode of flying. The sea wolves, too, in the Paulus Mæotis, do something of a very similar nature; but if they do not receive their fair share from the fishermen they will tear their nets as they lie extended. Hawks will not eat the heart of a bird.

Section XIII
THE GARDEN

The cultivation of the garden is a subject recommended by its own intrinsic merits to our notice: for we find that even in remote antiquity there was nothing looked upon with a greater degree of admiration than the gardens of the Hesperides, those of the kings Adonis and Alcinoüs, and the Hanging Gardens, whether they were the work of Semiramis, or whether of Cyrus king of Assyria. The kings of Rome cultivated their gardens with their own hands; indeed it was from his garden that Tarquinius Superbus sent to his son that cruel and sanguinary message of his. In our laws of the Twelve Tables we find the word "villa," or "farm," nowhere mentioned; it is the word "hortus" that is always used with that signification while the term "heredium" we find employed for "garden."

There are certain religious impressions, too, that have been attached to this species of property, and we find that it is in the garden and the Forum only that statues of satyrs are consecrated as a protection against the evil effects of spells and sorcery; although in Plautus we find the gardens spoken of as being under the tutelage of Venus. At the present day, under the general name of gardens, we have pleasure grounds situated in the very heart of the City as well as extensive fields and villas.

Epicurus, that connoisseur in the enjoyments of a life of ease, was the first to lay out a garden at Athens; up to his time it had never been thought of to dwell in the country in the middle of the town. At Rome on the other hand the garden constituted of itself the poor man's field, and it was from the garden that the lower classes procured their daily food—an aliment how guiltlessly obtained! But still it is a great deal better, no doubt, to dive into the abysses of the deep and to seek each kind of oyster at the risk and

125

peril of shipwreck, to go searching for birds beyond the river Phasis which, protected as they are by the terrors invented by fable, are only rendered all the more precious thereby—to go searching for others again in Numidia and the very sepulchres of Æthiopia, or else to be battling with wild beasts and to get eaten one's self while trying to take a prey which another person is to eat! And yet, by Hercules! how little do the productions of the garden cost us in comparison with these! How more than sufficient for every wish and for every want!—were it not indeed that here, as in every thing else, turn which way we will we find the same grounds for our wrath and indignation. We really might be content to allow of fruits being grown of the most exquisite quality, remarkable, some of them for their flavor, some for their size, some again for the monstrosities of their growth, morsels all of them forbidden to the poor! We might allow of wines being kept till they are mellowed with age or enfeebled by being passed through cloth strainers, of men, too, however prolonged their lives, never drinking any but a wine that is still older than themselves! We might allow of luxury devising how best to extract the very aroma and marrow only from grain; of people living upon nothing but the choicest productions of the confectioner and upon pastes fashioned in fantastic shapes: of one kind of bread being prepared for the rich and another for the multitude; of the yearly produce of the field being classified in a descending scale till it reaches the humble means of the very lowest classes—but do we not find that these refined distinctions have been extended to the very herbs and that riches have contrived to establish points of dissimilarity in articles of food which ordinarily sell for a single copper coin?

In this department humble as it is, we are still destined to find certain productions that are denied to the community at large, and the very cabbages pampered to such an enormous extent that the poor man's table is not large enough to hold them. Asparagus by Nature was in-

tended to grow wild so that each might gather it where he
pleased—but lo and behold! we find it in the highest state
of cultivation, and Ravenna produces heads that weigh as
much as three pounds! Alas for the monstrous excess of
gluttony! It would be surprising indeed for the beasts of
the field to be forbidden the thistle for food, and yet it is
a thing forbidden to the lower classes of the community!
These refined distinctions are extended to the very water
and, thanks to the mighty influence of money, there are
lines of demarcation drawn in the very elements themselves. Some persons are for drinking ice, others for
quaffing snow, and thus is the curse of the mountain steep
turned into an appetizing stimulus for the palate! Cold is
carefully treasured up for the summer heats, and man's invention is racked how best to keep snow freezing in
months that are not its own. Some again there are who
first boil the water, and then bring it to the temperature
of winter—indeed there is nothing that pleases man in the
fashion in which Nature originally made it.

And is it the fact then that any herb of the garden is
reared only for the rich man's table? It is so—but still let
no one of the angered populace think of a fresh secession
to Mount Sacer or Mount Aventine; for to a certainty, in
the long run all-powerful money will bring them back to
just the same position as they were in when it wrought the
severance. For, by Hercules! there was not an impost
levied at Rome more grievous than the market dues, an
impost that aroused the indignation of the populace, who
repeatedly appealed with loud clamors to all the chief men
of the state to be relieved from it. At last they were relieved from this heavy tax upon their wares; and then it
was found that there was no tax more lucrative, more readily collected, or less obnoxious to the caprices of chance
than the impost that was levied in exchange for it in the
shape of a property tax extended to the poorest classes: for
now the very soil itself is their surety that paid the tax will
be, their means are patent to the light of day and the super-

ficial extent of their possessions, whatever the weather
may chance to be, always remains the same.

Cato, we find, speaks in high praise of garden cabbages: indeed it was according to their respective methods
of garden cultivation that the agriculturists of early times
were appreciated, and it was immediately concluded that
it was a sign of a woman being a bad and careless manager
of her family when the kitchen garden—for this was
looked upon as the woman's department more particularly
—was negligently cultivated; as in such case her only resource was of course the shambles or the herb market. But
cabbages were not held in such high esteem in those days
as now: indeed all dishes were held in disrepute which required something else to help them down, the great object
being to economize oil as much as possible; and as to the
flesh market, so much as a wish even to taste its wares was
visited with censure and reproach. The chief thing that
made them so fond of the garden was the fact that its produce needs no fire and ensures economy in fuel, and that it
offers resources which are always ready and at hand. These
articles of food which from their peculiar nature we call
"vinegar diets" were found to be easy of digestion, by no
means apt to blunt and overload the senses, and to create
but little craving for bread as an accompaniment. A portion of them which is still used by us for seasonings attests
that our forefathers used only to look at home for their
resources, and that no Indian peppers were in request
with them or any of those other condiments which we are
in the habit of seeking beyond the seas. In former times
the lower classes of Rome with their mimic gardens in
their windows, day after day presented the reflex of the
country to the eye, when as yet the multitudes of atrocious
burglaries, almost innumerable, had not compelled us to
shut out all such sights with bars to the passers-by.

Let the garden have its due meed of honor, and let
not things, because they are common, enjoy for that the
less share of our consideration—and the more so as we find

that from it men of the very highest rank have been content to borrow their surnames; thus in the Valerian family for instance the Lactucini have not thought themselves disgraced by taking their name from the lettuce. Perhaps, too, our labors and research may contribute some slight recommendation to this our subject; although with Virgil we are ready to admit how difficult it is, by language however elevated, to ennoble a subject that is so humble in itself.

There is no doubt that the proper plan is to have the gardens adjoining the country house; and they should be watered more particularly by a river running in front of it if possible; or else with water drawn from a well by the aid of a wheel or of pumps or by swipes. The ground should be opened just as the west winds are beginning to prevail; fourteen days after which it should be got ready for autumn, and then before the winter solstice it should have another turning up. It will require eight men to dig a jugerum, manure being mixed with the earth to a depth of three feet: the ground should be divided into plots or beds with raised and rounded edges each of which should have a path dug round it by means of which access may be afforded to the gardener and a channel formed for the water needed for irrigation.

Among the garden plants there are some that recommend themselves by their bulbs, others by the head, others by the stalk, others by the leaf, others by both: some, again, are valued for their seed, others for the outer coat, others for their membranous tissues, others for their cartilaginous substance, others for the firmness of their flesh, and others for the fleshy tunics in which they are enveloped.

Of some plants the fruits are in the earth, of others both in the earth and out of it, and of others out of the earth solely. Some of them increase as they lie upon the ground, gourds and cucumbers, for instance; the same products will grow also in a hanging position but they are much heavier even then than any of the fruits that grow upon trees. The cucumber is composed of cartilage and a

fleshy substance, while the gourd consists of rind and cartilage: this last is the only vegetable production the outer
coat of which becomes of a ligneous nature when ripe.
Radishes, turnips, and rape are hidden in the earth, and
so, too, are elecampane, skirrets, and parsnips, though in
a different manner. There are some plants to which we
shall give the name of "ferulaceous," anise and mallows for
instance; indeed we find it stated by some writers that in
Arabia the mallow becomes arborescent at the sixth month,
so much so in fact as to admit of its being used for walking
sticks. We have another instance in the mallow tree of
Mauretania which is found at Lixus, a city built upon an
æstuary there; and at which spot, it is said, were formerly
the gardens of the Hesperides, at a distance of two hundred
paces from the Ocean. This mallow tree is twenty feet in
height and of such a thickness that there is not a person in
existence who is able with his arms to span its girth.

The cucumber belongs to the cartilaginous class of
plants, and grows above the ground. It was a wonderful
favorite with the Emperor Tiberius, and indeed he was
never without it; for he had raised beds made in frames
upon wheels, by means of which the cucumbers were
moved and exposed to the full heat of the sun; while in
winter they were withdrawn and placed under the protection of frames glazed with mirrorstone.

Storage

Apples and pears are prepared for keeping just like
grapes, and in as many different ways; but with the exception of plums they are the only fruit stored in casks. Apples
and pears have certain vinous properties, and like wine
these drinks are forbidden to invalids by the physicians.
These fruits are sometimes boiled up with wine and water,
and so make a preserve that is eaten with bread; a preparation which is never made of any other fruit, with the ex-

ception of the quinces known as the "cotoneum" and the "strutheum."

For the better preserving of fruits it is universally rec-ommended that the storeroom should be situated in a cool, dry spot, with a well-boarded floor and windows looking towards the north, which in fine weather ought to be kept open. Care should also be taken to keep out the south wind by window panes, while at the same time it should be borne in mind that a northeast wind will shrivel fruit and make it unsightly. Apples are gathered after the autumnal equinox; but the gathering should never begin before the sixteenth day of the moon or before the first hour of the day. Windfalls should always be kept separate, and there ought to be a layer of straw or else mats or chaff placed beneath. They should also be placed apart from each other in rows so that the air may circulate freely between them, and they may equally gain the benefit of it. The Amerin-ian apple is the best keeper, the melimelum the very worst of all.

Quinces ought to be stored in a place kept perfectly closed so as to exclude all draughts; or else they should be boiled in honey or soaked in it. Pomegranates are made hard and firm by being first put in boiling sea water, and then left to dry for three days in the sun, care being taken that the dews of the night do not touch them; after which they are hung up, and when wanted for use, washed with fresh water. M. Varro recommends that they should be kept in large vessels filled with sand: if they are not ripe, he says that they should be put in pots with the bottom broken out, and then buried in the earth, all access to the air being carefully shut, and care being first taken to cover the stalk with pitch. By this mode of treatment, he assures us, they will attain a larger size than they would if left to ripen on the tree. As for the other kinds of pomes, he says that they should be wrapped up separately in fig leaves, the windfalls being carefully excluded, and then stored in baskets of osier, or else covered over with potters' earth.

Pears are kept in earthen vessels pitched inside; when filled the vessels are reversed and then buried in pits. The Tarentine pear, Varro says, is gathered very late, while the Anician keeps very well in raisin wine. Sorb apples are similarly kept in holes in the ground, the vessel being turned upside down and a layer of plaster placed on the lid: it should be buried two feet deep in a sunny spot; sorbs are also hung, like grapes, in the inside of large vessels, together with the branches.

Some of the more recent authors are found to pay a more scrupulous degree of attention to these various particulars, and recommend that the gathering of grapes or pomes which are intended for keeping should take place while the moon is on the wane, after the third hour of the day and while the weather is clear or dry winds prevail. In a similar manner the selection, they say, ought to be made from a dry spot, and the fruit should be plucked before it is fully ripe, a moment being chosen while the moon is below the horizon. Grapes, they say, should be selected that have a strong, hard mallet stalk, and after the decayed berries have been carefully removed with a pair of scissors they should be hung up inside of a large vessel which has just been pitched, care being taken to close all access to the south wind by covering the lid with a coat of plaster. The same method, they say, should be adopted for keeping apples and pears, the stalks being carefully covered with pitch; care should be taken that the vessels are kept at a distance from water.

There are some persons who adopt the following method for preserving grapes. They take them off together with the branch and place them, while still upon it, in a layer of plaster, taking care to fasten either end of the branch in a bulb of squill. Others go so far as to place them within vessels containing wine, taking care however that the grapes as they hang do not touch it. Some persons put apples in plates of earth and then leave them to float in wine, a method by which it is thought that a vinous flavor is imparted to them: while some think it a better plan to preserve all these kinds of fruit in millet. Most people, however, content themselves with first digging a hole in the ground, a couple of feet in depth; a layer of sand is then placed at the bottom and the fruit is arranged upon it and covered with an earthen lid, over which the earth is thrown. Some persons again even go so far as to give their grapes a coating of potters' chalk, and then hang them up when dried in the sun; when required for use, the chalk is removed with water. Apples are also preserved in a similar manner; but with them wine is employed for getting off the chalk. Indeed we find a very similar plan pursued with apples of the finest quality; they have a coating laid upon them of either plaster or wax; but they are apt, if not quite ripe when this was done, by the increase in their size to break their casing. When apples are thus prepared they are always laid with the stalk downwards. Some persons pluck the apple together with the branch, the ends of which they thrust into the pith of elder and then bury it in the way already pointed out. There are some who assign to each apple or pear its separate vessel of clay, and after carefully pitching the cover, enclose it again in a larger vessel: occasionally the fruit is placed on a layer of wool or else in baskets with a lining of chaff and clay. Other persons follow a similar plan but use earthen plates for the purpose; while others employ the same method but dig a hole in the earth, and after placing a layer of sand, lay the fruit on top of it and then cover the whole with dry earth. Persons are sometimes known to give quinces a coating of Pontic wax, and then plunge them in honey.

Columella informs us that fruit is kept by being carefully put in earthen vessels which then receive a coating of pitch and are placed in wells or cisterns to sink to the bottom. The people of maritime Liguria, in the vicinity of the Alps first dry their grapes in the sun, and wrap them up in bundles of rushes which are then covered with plaster. The Greeks follow a similar plan, but substitute for rushes the leaves of the planetree or of the vine or the fig, which they dry for a single day in the shade and then place in a cask in alternate layers with husks of grapes. It is by this method that they preserve the grapes of Cos and Berytus which are inferior to none in sweetness. Some persons when thus preparing them plunge the grapes into lye ashes the moment they take them from the vine, and then dry them in the sun; they then steep them in warm water, after which they put them to dry again in the sun: and last of all, wrap them up in bundles formed of layers of leaves and grape husks. There are some who prefer keeping their grapes in sawdust, or else in shavings of the fir tree, poplar, and ash: while others think it the best plan to hang them up in the granary at a careful distance from the apples directly after the gathering, being under the impression that the very best covering for them as they hang is the dust that naturally arises.

Grafting

Nature has taught us the art of grafting by means of seed. We see a seed swallowed whole by a famished bird; when softened by the natural heat of the crop it is voided, with the fecundating juices of the dung, upon some soft couch formed by a tree; or else, as is often the case, is carried by the winds to some cleft in the bark of a tree. Hence it is that we see the cherry growing upon the willow, the plane upon the laurel, the laurel upon the cherry, and fruits of various tints and hues all springing from the same tree at once. It is said, too, that the jackdaw, from its conceal-ment of the seeds of plants in holes which serve as its store-houses, gives rise to a similar result.

In this the art of inoculating took its rise. By the aid of an instrument similar to a shoemaker's paring knife an eye is opened in a tree by paring away the bark, and an-other bud is then enclosed in it, that has been previously removed with the same instrument from another tree. This was the ancient mode of inoculation with the fig and the apple. That, described by Virgil, requires a slight fissure to be made in the knot of a bud which has burst through the bark, and in this is enclosed a bud taken from another tree. Thus far has Nature been our instructor in these matters.

A different mode of engrafting has been taught us by chance, another great instructor, and one from whom, perhaps, we have learnt a still greater number of lessons. A careful husbandman, being desirous, for its better protection, to surround his cottage with a palisade thrust the stakes into growing ivy in order to prevent them from rotting. Seized by the tenacious grasp of the still living ivy the stakes borrowed life from the life of another wood, and it was found that the stock of a tree acted in place of earth.

Cabbage

Cabbage and coleworts, which at the present day are the most highly esteemed of all the garden vegetables, were held in little repute, I find, among the Greeks; but Cato on the other hand sings the wondrous praises of the cabbage. Cato distinguishes three varieties of the cabbage; the first, a plant with leaves wide open and a large stalk; a second, with crisped leaves, to which he gives the name of "Apiaca," and a third, with a thin stalk and a smooth, tender leaf, which with him ranks the lowest of all.

Cabbages may be sown the whole year through as we find that they are cut at all periods of the year; the best time, however, for sowing them is at the autumnal equinox, and they are usually transplanted as soon as five leaves are visible. In the ensuing spring after the first cutting the plant yields sprouts, known to us as "cymæ." These sprouts are small shoots thrown out from the main stem, of a more delicate and tender quality than the cabbage itself. The exquisite palate, however, of Apicius rejected these sprouts for the table, and his example was followed by the fastidious Drusus Cæsar, who did not escape, however, the censures of his father Tiberius for being so over-nice. After the cymæ have made their appearance the cabbage throws out its summer and autumn shoots and then its winter ones; after which a new crop of cymæ is produced, there being no plant so productive as this, until at last it is quite exhausted by its extreme fertility. A second time for sowing cabbages is immediately after the vernal equinox, the plants of this growth being transplanted at the end of spring, that they may not run up into sprouts before coming to a top: and a third sowing takes place about the summer solstice, the transplanting being done in summer if the soil is moist but, if too dry, in autumn. When moisture and manure are supplied in small quantities the flavor of the cabbage is all the more agreeable, but when they are supplied in greater abundance the plants attain a larger size. Asses' dung is the best adapted for its growth.

The cabbage is one of those articles so highly esteemed by epicures; for which reason it will not be amiss if we speak of it at somewhat greater length. To obtain plants equally remarkable for their size and flavor, care must be taken first of all to sow the seed in ground that has had a couple of turnings up, and then to follow up the shoots as they appear above ground by molding them up, care being taken to throw up the earth over them as they increase in luxuriance and to let nothing but the summit appear above the surface. This kind is known as the Tritian cabbage: in money and labor it costs twice as much as any of the others.

The other varieties of the cabbage are numerous—there is the Cumanian cabbage with leaves that lie close to the ground and a wide, open head; the Aricinian cabbage, of no greater height but with more numerous leaves and thinner—this last is looked upon as the most useful of them all, for beneath nearly all of the leaves there are small shoots thrown out, peculiar to this variety. The cabbage of Pompeii is considerably taller, the stalk, which is thin at the root, increasing in thickness as it rises among the leaves, which are fewer in number and narrower; the great merit of this cabbage is its remarkable tenderness, although it is not able to stand the cold. The cabbage of Bruttium on the other hand thrives all the better for cold; the leaves of it are remarkably large, the stalk thin, and the flavor pungent. The leaves of the Sabine cabbage are crisped to such a degree as to excite our surprise, and their thickness is such as to quite exhaust the stem; in sweetness it is said to surpass all the others.

There have lately come into fashion the cabbages known as the "Lacuturres"; they are grown in the valley of Aricia where there was formerly a lake, now no longer in existence, and a tower which is still standing. The head of this cabbage is very large and the leaves are almost without number, some of them being round and smooth, and others long and sinewy; indeed there is no cabbage that runs to a larger head than this, with the sole exception of the Tritian variety which has a head sometimes as much as a foot in thickness and throws out its cymæ the latest of all.

In all kinds of cabbages, hoarfrost contributes very materially to their sweetness; but it is apt to be productive of considerable injury if care is not taken to protect the pith by cutting them aslant. Those plants which are intended for seed are never cut.

There is another kind that is held in peculiar esteem, and which never exceeds the height of an herbaceous plant; it is known by the name of "halmyridia" from the circumstance of its growing on the seashore only. It will keep green and fresh during a long voyage if care is taken not to let it touch the ground from the moment that it is cut, but to put it into oil vessels lately dried and then to bung them so as to effectually exclude all air. There are some who are of opinion that the plant will come to maturity all the sooner if some seaweed is laid at the root when it is transplanted, or else as much pounded niter as can be taken up with three fingers; and others, again, sprinkle the leaves with trefoil seed and niter pounded together. Niter preserves the greenness of cabbage when cooked, a result which is equally ensured by the Apician mode of boiling, or in other words, by steeping the plants in oil and salt before they are cooked.

There is a method of grafting vegetables by cutting the shoots and the stalk and then inserting in the pith the seed of another plant; a plan which has been adopted with the wild cucumber. There is another kind of wild cabbage, the lapsana, which has become famous since the triumphs of the late Emperor Julius, in consequence of the songs and jokes of his soldiers more particularly; for in the alternate lines sung by them they used to reproach him for having made them live on lapsana at the siege of Dyrrhachium and to rally him upon the parsimonious scale on which he was in the habit of recompensing their services.

Section XIV
ROME

It is now time to pass on to the marvels in building displayed by our own City, and to make some inquiry into the resources and experience that we have gained in the lapse of eight hundred years; and so prove that here the rest of the world has been outdone by us: a thing which will appear to have occurred almost as many times as the marvels are in number which I shall have to enumerate. If all the buildings of our City are considered in the aggregate, and supposing them all thrown together in one vast mass, the united grandeur of them would lead one to suppose that we were describing another world, accumulated in a single spot.

Not to mention among our great work the Circus Maximus that was constructed by the Dictator Cæsar, one stadium in width and three in length and occupying, with the adjacent buildings, no less than four jugera, with room for two hundred and sixty thousand spectators seated; am I not to include in the number of our magnificent constructions the Basilica of Paulus with its admirable Phrygian columns; the Forum of the late Emperor Augustus; the Temple of Peace erected by the Emperor Vespasianus Augustus— some of the finest works that the world has ever beheld —the roofing, too, of the Vote-Office that was built by Agrippa? not to forget that, before his time, Valerius of Ostia the architect had covered over a theater at Rome at the time of the public Games celebrated by Libo?

We behold with admiration pyramids that were built by kings, when the very ground alone that was purchased by the Dictator Cæsar for the construction of his Forum cost one hundred millions of sesterces! If an enormous expenditure has its attractions for any one whose mind is influenced by monetary considerations, be it known to him

that the house in which Clodius dwelt, who was slain by
Milo, was purchased by him at the price of fourteen million
eight hundred thousand sesterces! a thing that, for my part,
I look upon as no less astounding than the monstrous follies
that have been displayed by kings. And then, as to Milo
himself, the sums in which he was indebted amounted to
no less than seventy millions of sesterces; a state of things,
to be considered, in my opinion, as one of the most portentous phænomena in the history of the human mind. But
it was in those days that old men still spoke in admiration
of the vast proportions of the Agger and of the enormous
foundation of the Capitol; of the public sewers, too, a work
more stupendous than any; as mountains had to be pierced
for their construction, and navigation had to be carried on
beneath Rome; an event which happened in the ædileship
of M. Agrippa after he had filled the office of consul.

For this purpose there are seven rivers made, by artificial channels, to flow beneath the city. Rushing onward
like so many impetuous torrents they are compelled to
carry off and sweep away all the sewerage; and swollen
as they are by the vast accession of the pluvial waters
they reverberate against the sides and bottom of their channels. Occasionally, too, the Tiber, overflowing, is thrown
backward in its course and discharges itself by these out-
lets: obstinate is the contest that ensues within between the
meeting tides, but so firm and solid is the masonry that it is
enabled to offer an effectual resistance. Enormous as are
the accumulations that are carried along above, the work
of the channels never gives way. Houses falling sponta-
neously to ruins or leveled with the ground by conflagrations are continually battering against them; the ground is
shaken by earthquakes every now and then; and yet, built
as they were in the days of Tarquinius Priscus seven hundred years ago, these constructions have survived all but
unharmed. We must not omit to mention one remarkable
circumstance, and all the more remarkable from the fact
that the most celebrated historians have omitted to mention

it. Tarquinius Priscus having commenced the sewers and set the lower classes to work upon them, the laboriousness and prolonged duration of the employment became equally an object of dread to them; and the consequence was that suicide was a thing of common occurrence, the citizens adopting this method of escaping their troubles. For this evil the king devised a singular remedy, and one that has never been resorted to either before that time or since: for he ordered the bodies of all who had been thus guilty of self-destruction to be fastened to a cross and left there as a spectacle to their fellow citizens and a prey to birds and wild beasts. The result was that that sense of propriety which so peculiarly attaches itself to the Roman name, and which more than once has gained a victory when the battle was all but lost came to the rescue on this occasion as well; though for this once the Romans were in reality its dupes, as they forgot that, though they felt shocked at the thoughts of such ignominy while alive, they would be quite insensible to any such disgrace when dead. It is said that Tarquinius made these sewers of dimensions sufficiently large to admit of a wagon laden with hay passing along them.

All that we have just described, however, is but trifling when placed in comparison with one marvelous fact which I must not omit to mention before I pass on to other subjects. In the consulship of M. Lepidus and Q. Catulus there was not at Rome, as we learn from the most trustworthy authors, a finer house than the one which belonged to Lepidus himself: and yet, by Hercules! within five-and-thirty years from that period the very same house did not hold the hundredth rank even in the City! Let a person in taking this fact into consideration only calculate the vast masses of marble, the productions of painters, the regal treasures that must have been expended in bringing these hundred mansions to vie with one that had been in its day the most sumptuous and the most celebrated in all the City; and then let him reflect how that, since that period and down to the present time, these houses have all of them been surpassed by others without number. There can be no doubt that conflagrations are a punishment inflicted upon us for our luxury; but such are out habits that in spite of such warning as these we cannot be made to understand that there are things in existence more perishable even than man himself.

But there are still two other mansions by which all these edifices have been eclipsed. Twice have we seen the whole City enclosed by the palaces of the Emperors Caius and Nero; that of the last, that nothing might be wanting to its magnificence, being coated with gold. Surely such palaces as these must have been intended for the abode of those who created this mighty empire and who left the plough or their native hearth to go forth to conquer nations and to return laden with triumphs! men, in fact, whose fields occupied less space than the audience chambers of these palaces.

I will not permit these two to enjoy this glory, such as it is; for I will prove that these extravagant follies of theirs have been surpassed in the use that was made of his wealth by M. Scaurus, a private citizen. Indeed I am by no means certain that it was not the ædileship of this person that inflicted the first great blow upon the public manners, and that Sylla was not guilty of a greater crime in giving such unlimited power to his stepson than in the proscription of so many thousands. During his ædileship, and only for the temporary purposes of a few days, Scaurus executed the greatest work that has ever been made by the hands of man, even when intended to be of everlasting duration; his Theater, I mean. This building consisted of three stories, supported upon three hundred and sixty columns; and this in a city which had not allowed without some censure one of its greatest citizens to erect six pillars of Hymettian marble. The ground story was of marble, the second of glass, a species of luxury which ever since that time has been quite unheard of, and the highest of gilded wood. The lowermost columns were eight-and-thirty feet in height;

and placed between these columns were brazen statues, three thousand in number. The area of this theater afforded accommodation for eighty thousand spectators; and yet the Theater of Pompeius, after the City had so greatly increased and the inhabitants had become so vastly more numerous, was considered large enough, with its sittings for forty thousand only. The rest of the fittings of it, what with Attalic vestments, pictures, and the other stage properties, were of such enormous value that, after Scaurus had had conveyed to his Tusculan villa such parts thereof as were not required for the enjoyment of his daily luxuries, the loss was no less than three hundred millions of sesterces when the villa was burnt by his servants in a spirit of revenge.

The consideration of such prodigality as this quite distracts my attention and compels me to digress from my original purpose in order to mention a still greater instance of extravagance in reference to wood. C. Curio who died during the civil wars, fighting on the side of Cæsar, found to his dismay that he could not, when celebrating the funeral games in honor of his father, surpass the riches and magnificence of Scaurus—for where was to be found such a stepsire as Sylla, and such a mother as Metella, that bidder at all auctions for the property of the proscribed? Where, too, was he to find for his father, M. Scaurus, so long the principal man in the city and one who had acted, in his alliance with Marius, as a receptacle for the plunder of whole provinces? Indeed, Scaurus himself was now no longer able to rival himself; and it was at least one advantage which he derived from this destruction by fire of so many objects brought from all parts of the earth that no one could ever after be his equal in this species of folly. Curio found himself compelled to fall back upon his own resources, and to think of some new device of his own.

He caused to be erected, close together, two theaters of very large dimensions and built of wood, each of them nicely poised and turning on a pivot. Before midday a

spectacle of games was exhibited in each; the theaters being
turned back to back in order that the noise of neither of
them might interfere with what was going on in the other.
Then in the latter part of the day the two theaters were
swung round and, the corners uniting, brought face to face;
the outer frames were removed, and thus an amphitheater
was formed in which combats of gladiators were presented
to view; men whose safety was almost less compromised
than was that of the Roman people in allowing itself to be
thus whirled round from side to side. Now in this case
which have we most reason to admire, the inventor or the
invention? the artist or the author of the project? him who
first dared to think of such an enterprise, or him who ven-
tured to undertake it? him who obeyed the order, or him
who gave it? But the thing that surpasses all is the frenzy
that must have possessed the public to take their seats in a
place which must of necessity have been so unsubstantial
and so insecure. Lo and behold! here is a people that has
conquered the whole earth, that has subdued the universe,
that divides the spoils of kingdoms and of nations, that
sends its laws to foreign lands, that shares in some degree
the attributes of the immortal gods in common with mankind, suspended aloft in a machine, and showering plaudits
even upon its own peril!

This is indeed holding life cheap; and can we, after
this, complain of our disasters at Cannæ? How vast the
catastrophe that might have ensued! When cities are swallowed up by an earthquake it is looked upon by mankind as
a general calamity; and yet here have we the whole Roman
people embarked, so to say, in two ships and sitting suspended on a couple of pivots; the grand spectacle being its
own struggle with danger and its liability to perish at any
moment that the overstrained machinery may give way!
And then the object, too, of all this—that public favor may
be conciliated for the tribune's harangues at a future day,
and that at the Rostra he may still have the power of shaking the tribes, nicely balanced as they are! And really what

may he not dare with those who at his persuasion have braved such perils as these? Indeed, to confess the truth, at the funeral games celebrated at the tomb of his father it was no less than the whole Roman people that shared the dangers of the gladiatorial combats. When the pivots had now been sufficiently worked and wearied he gave another turn to his magnificent displays. For upon the last day, still preserving the form of the amphitheater he cut the stage in two through the middle, and exhibited a spectacle of athletes; after which, the stage being suddenly withdrawn on either side he exhibited a combat upon the same day between such of the gladiators as had previously proved victorious. And yet with all this Curio was no king, no ruler of the destinies of a nation, nor yet a person remarkable for his opulence; seeing that he possessed no resources of his own beyond what he could realize from the discord between the leading men.

But let us now turn our attention to some marvels which, justly appreciated, may be truthfully pronounced to remain unsurpassed. Q. Marcius Rex upon being commanded by the senate to repair the Appian Aqueduct and those of the Anio and Tepula constructed during his prætorship a new aqueduct which bore his name and was brought hither by a channel pierced through the sides of mountains. Agrippa in his ædileship united the Marcian with the Virgin Aqueduct, and repaired and strengthened the channels of the others. He also formed seven hundred wells, in addition to five hundred fountains and one hundred and thirty reservoirs, many of them magnificently adorned. Upon these works he erected three hundred statues of marble or bronze and four hundred marble columns; and all this in the space of a single year! In the work which he has written in commemoration of his ædileship he also informs us that public games were celebrated for the space of fifty-nine days, and that one hundred and seventy public baths were opened. The number of these last at Rome has increased to an infinite extent since his time.

The preceding aqueducts have all been surpassed by the costly work which was more recently commenced by the Emperor Caius and completed by Claudius. Under these princes the Curtian and Cærulean Waters, with the New Anio, were brought from a distance of forty miles and at so high a level that all the hills were supplied with water, on which the City is built. The sum expended on these works was three hundred and fifty millions of sesterces. If we take into consideration the abundant supply of water to the public for baths, ponds, canals, household purposes, gardens, places in the suburbs, and country houses; and then reflect upon the distances that are traversed, the arches that have been constructed, the mountains that have been pierced, the valleys that have been leveled, we must admit that there is nothing to be found more worthy of our admiration throughout the whole universe.

Among the most memorable works I should include another undertaking of the Emperor Claudius, although it was afterwards abandoned in consequence of the hatred borne him by his successor. I mean the channel that was cut through a mountain as an outlet for Lake Fucinus, a work which cost a sum beyond all calculation and employed a countless multitude of workmen for many years. In some parts it was necessary to pump up the water by the aid of machinery; in other parts the solid rock had to be hewn through. All this had to be done in the midst of darkness within; a series of operations which can only be adequately conceived by those who were witnesses of them, and which no human language can possibly describe.

I pass in silence the harbor that has been formed at Ostia; the various roads that have been cut across mountains; the Tyrrhenian Sea separated by an embankment from Lake Lucrinus; and vast numbers of bridges constructed at an enormous expense.

THE ARTS

Painting

I shall begin with what still remains to be said with reference to painting, an art which was formerly illustrious when it was held in esteem both by kings and peoples, and ennobling those whom it deigned to transmit to posterity. But at the present day it is completely banished in favor of marble, and even gold. For not only are whole walls now covered with marble, but the marble itself is carved out or else inlaid so as to represent objects and animals of various kinds. No longer now are we satisfied with formal panels of marble, or with slabs extended like so many mountains in our chambers, but we must begin to paint the very stone itself! This art was invented in the reign of Claudius, but it was in the time of Nero that we discovered the method of inserting in marble spots that do not belong to it, and so varying its uniformity; and this, for the purpose of representing the marble of Numidia variegated with ovals, and that of Synnada veined with purple; just as luxury might have willed that Nature should produce them. Such are our resources when the quarries fail us, and luxury ceases not to busy itself, in order that as much as possible may be lost whenever a conflagration happens.

Correct portraits of individuals were formerly transmitted to future ages by painting; but this has now completely fallen into desuetude. Brazen shields are now set up, and silver faces with only some obscure traces of the countenance: the very heads of statues are changed, a thing that has given rise before now to many a current sarcastic line; so true it is that people prefer showing off the valuable material to having a faithful likeness. And yet at the same time we tapestry the walls of our galleries with old pictures, and we prize the portraits of strangers; while those made in honor of ourselves we esteem only for the value of the material, for some heir to break up and melt and so forestall the noose and slipknot of the thief. Thus it is that we possess the portraits of no living individuals, and leave behind us the pictures of our wealth, not of our persons.

And yet the very same persons adorn the palæstra and the anointing room with portraits of athletes, and hang up in their chamber and carry about them a likeness of Epicurus. On the twentieth day of each moon they celebrate his birthday by a sacrifice, and keep his festival known as the "Icas" every month: and these, too, people who wish to live without being known! So it is, most assuredly, our indolence has lost sight of the arts, and since our minds are distitute of any characteristic features, those of our bodies are neglected also.

But on the contrary, in the days of our ancestors it was these that were to be seen in their halls, and not statues made by foreign artists or works in bronze or marble: portraits modeled in wax were arranged, each in its separate niche, to be always in readiness to accompany the funeral processions of the family; occasions on which every member of the family that had ever existed was always present. The pedigree of the individual was traced in lines upon each of these colored portraits. Their muniment rooms, too, were filled with archives and memoirs stating what each had done when holding the magistracy. On the outside of their houses and around the thresholds of their doors were placed other statues of those mighty spirits, in the spoils of the enemy there affixed, memorials which a purchaser was not allowed to displace; so that the house continued to triumph even after it had changed its master. A powerful stimulus to emulation this, when the walls each day reproached an unwarlike owner for having thus intruded upon the triumphs of another! There is still extant an address by the orator Messala, full of indignation, in which he forbids that there should be inserted among the

images of his family any of those of the stranger race of the
Lævini. It was the same feeling that extorted from old Messala those compilations of his "On the Families of Rome";
when, upon passing through the hall of Scipio Pomponianus, he observed that in consequence of a testamentary
adoption the Salvittos—for that had been their surname—to
the disgrace of the Africani, had surreptitiously contrived
to assume the name of the Scipios. But the Messalas must
pardon me if I remark that to lay a claim, though an un-
truthful one, to the statues of illustrious men shows some
love for their virtues and is much more honorable than to
have such a character as to merit that no one should wish
to claim them.

There is a new invention too, which we must not omit
to notice. Not only do we consecrate in our libraries, in
gold or silver or in bronze, those whose immortal spirits
hold converse with us in those places, but we even go so far
as to reproduce the ideal of features, all remembrance of
which has ceased to exist; and our regrets give existence to
likenesses that have not been transmitted to us, as in the
case of Homer, for example. And indeed it is my opinion
that nothing can be a greater proof of having achieved
success in life than a lasting desire on the part of one's
fellow men to know what one's features were. This practice of grouping portraits was first introduced at Rome
by Asinius Pollio who was also the first to establish a public
library, and so make the works of genius the property of
the public. Whether the kings of Alexandria and of Pergamus, who had so energetically rivaled each other in
forming libraries, had previously introduced this practice
I cannot so easily say.

That a strong passion for portraits formerly existed is
attested both by Atticus, the friend of Cicero, who wrote a
work on this subject, and by M. Varro who conceived the
idea of inserting, by some means or other, in his numerous
volumes the portraits of seven hundred individuals; as he
could not bear the idea that all traces of their features

should be lost or that the lapse of centuries should get the better of mankind. Thus was he the inventor of a benefit to his fellow men that might have been envied by the gods themselves; for not only did he confer upon them immortality, but he transmitted them to all parts of the earth; so that everywhere it might be possible for them to be present and for each to occupy his niche. This service, too, Varro conferred upon persons who were no members of his own family.

So far as I can learn, Appius Claudius who was consul with P. Servilius was the first to dedicate shields in honor of his own family in a sacred or public place. For he placed representations of his ancestors in the Temple of Bellona and desired that they might be erected in an elevated spot, so as to be seen, and the inscriptions reciting their honors read. A truly graceful device; more particularly when a multitude of children, represented by so many tiny figures, displays those germs, as it were, which are destined to continue the line: shields such as these no one can look at without a feeling of pleasure and lively interest.

More recently M. Æmilius who was consul with Quintus Lutatius not only erected these shields in the Æmilian Basilica but in his own house as well; in doing which he followed a truly warlike example. For these portraits were represented on bucklers similar to those used in the Trojan War; and hence it is that these shields received their present name of "clypei," and not, as the perverse subtleties of the grammarians will have it, from the word "cluo." It was an abundant motive for valor when upon each shield was represented the features of him who had borne it. The Carthaginians used to make both their bucklers and their portraits of gold and to carry them with them in the camp: at all events, Marcius the avenger of the Scipios in Spain found one of this kind on capturing the camp of Hasdrubal, and it was this same buckler that remained suspended over the gate of the Capitoline Temple until the time when it was first burnt. Indeed in the days of our ancestors, so assured was the safety of these shields that it has been a subject of remark, that in the consulship of L. Manlius and Q. Fulvius, M. Aufidius who had given security for the safety of the Capitol informed the senate that the bucklers there which had been assessed as copper, were in reality made of silver.

We have, by Pamphilus, a picture representing the Alliance and the Battle that was fought at Phlius; the Victory also that was gained by the Athenians, and a representation of Ulysses in his ship. He was a Macedonian by birth but was the first painter who was also skilled in all the other sciences, arithmetic and geometry more particularly, without the aid of which he maintained that the pictorial art could not attain perfection. He gave instruction to no one for a smaller sum than one talent, at the rate of five hundred denarii per annum, and this fee both Apelles and Melanthius paid. It was through his influence that, first at Sicyon and then throughout the whole of Greece, all children of free birth were taught the graphic art, or in other words the art of depicting upon boxwood, before all others; in consequence of which this came to be looked upon as the first step in the liberal arts. It is the fact, however, that this art has always been held in high estimation, and cultivated by persons of free birth, and that at a more recent period men of rank began to pursue it; it having always been forbidden that slaves should receive instruction in it. Hence it is, that neither in painting nor in carving has there been any celebrated work executed by a slave.

It was Apelles of Cos, in the hundred and twelfth Olympiad, who surpassed all the other painters who either preceded or succeeded him. Singlehanded he contributed more to painting than all the others together and even went so far as to publish some treatises on the principles of the art. The great point of artistic merit with him was his singular charm of gracefulness, and this too, though the greatest of painters were his contemporaries. In admiring their works and bestowing high eulogiums upon them he used to say that there was still wanting in them that ideal of beauty so peculiar to himself, and known to the Greeks as "Charis"; others, he said, had acquired all the other requisites of perfection, but in this one point he himself had no equal. He also asserted his claim to another great point of merit: admiring a picture by Protogenes, which bore evident marks of unbounded laboriousness and the most minute finish, he remarked that in every respect Protogenes was fully his equal or perhaps his superior except in this that he himself knew when to take his hand off a picture —a memorable lesson which teaches us that overcarefulness may be productive of bad results.

A circumstance that happened to him in connection with Protogenes is worthy of notice. The latter was living at Rhodes when Apelles disembarked there, desirous of seeing the works of a man whom he had hitherto only known by reputation. Accordingly he repaired at once to the studio; Protogenes was not at home, but there happened to be a large panel upon the easel ready for painting, with an old woman who was left in charge. To his inquiries she made answer that Protogenes was not at home and then asked whom she should name as the visitor. "Here he is," was the reply of Apelles, and seizing a brush he traced with color upon the panel an outline of a singularly minute fineness. Upon his return the old woman mentioned to Protogenes what had happened. The artist, it is said, upon remarking the delicacy of the touch instantly exclaimed that Apelles must have been the visitor, for that no other person was capable of executing anything so exquisitely perfect. So saying, he traced within the same outline a still finer outline but with another color and then took his departure, with instructions to the woman to show it to the stranger if he returned, and to let him know that this was the person whom he had come to see. It happened as he anticipated; Apelles returned, and vexed at finding himself thus surpassed, he took up another color and split both of the outlines, leaving no possibility of anything finer being executed. Upon seeing this, Protogenes admitted that he was defeated and at once flew to the harbor to look for his guest. He thought proper, too, to transmit the panel to posterity just as it was, and it always continued to be held in the highest admiration by all, artists in particular. I am told that it was burnt in the first fire which took place at Cæsar's palace on the Palatine Hill; but in former times I have often stopped to admire it. Upon its vast surface it contained nothing whatever except the three outlines so remarkably fine as to escape the sight: among the most elaborate works of numerous other artists it had all the appearance of a blank space; and yet by that very fact it attracted the notice of every one and was held in higher estimation than any other painting there.

It was a custom with Apelles, to which he most tenaciously adhered, never to let any day pass, however busy he might be, without exercising himself by tracing some outline or other; a practice which has now passed into a proverb. It was also a practice with him when he had completed a work, to exhibit it to the view of the passers-by in some exposed place; while he himself, concealed behind the picture, would listen to the criticisms that were passed upon it; it being his opinion that the judgment of the public was preferable to his own as being the more discerning of the two. It was under these circumstances, they say, that he was censured by a shoemaker for having represented the shoes with one shoestring too little. The next day the shoemaker, quite proud at seeing the former error corrected, thanks to his advice, began to criticize the leg; upon which Apelles, full of indignation, popped his head out and reminded him that a shoemaker should give no opinion beyond the shoes, a piece of advice which has equally passed into a proverbial saying. In fact, Apelles was a person of great amenity of manners, a circumstance which rendered him particularly agreeable to Alexander the Great, who would often come to his studio. He had forbidden himself, by public edict, to be represented by any other artist. On one occasion however when the prince was in his studio, talking a great deal about painting without knowing anything about it, Apelles quietly begged that he would quit the subject, telling him that he would get laughed at by the boys who were there grinding the colors: so great was the influence which he rightfully possessed over a monarch who was otherwise of an irascible temperament. And yet, irascible as he was, Alexander conferred upon him a very signal mark of the high estimation in which he held him; for having, in his admiration of her extraordinary beauty, engaged Apelles to paint Pancaste undraped, the most beloved of all his concubines, the artist while so engaged fell in love with her; upon which, Alexander, perceiving this to be the case, made him a present of her, thus showing himself, though a great king in courage, a still greater one in self-command, this action redounding no less to his honor than any of his victories. For in thus conquering himself, not only did he sacrifice his passions in favor of the artist but even his affections as well; uninfluenced, too, by the feelings which must have possessed his favorite in this passing at once from the arms of a monarch to those of a painter. Some persons are of opinion that Pancaste was the model of Apelles in his painting of Venus Anadyomene.

It was Apelles who, courteous even to his rivals, first established the reputation of Protogenes at Rhodes. Held as he was in little estimation by his own fellow countrymen, a thing that generally is the case, Apelles inquired of him what price he set upon certain finished works of his which he had on hand. Upon Protogenes mentioning some very trifling sum or other, Apelles made him an offer of fifty talents and then circulated a report that he was buying these works in order to sell them as his own. By this contrivance he aroused the Rhodians to a better appreciation of the merits of their artist, and only consented to leave the pictures with them upon their offering a still larger price.

He painted portraits so exactly to the life that a fact with which we are made acquainted by the writings of

Apion the grammarian seems altogether incredible. One of those persons, he says, who divine events by the traits of the features, and are known as "metoposcopi," was enabled by an examination of his portraits to tell the year of the death, whether past or future, of each person represented. Apelles had been on bad terms with Ptolemæus in former times when they formed part of the suite of Alexander. After Ptolemæus had become king of Egypt it so happened that Apelles was driven by the violence of a tempest to Alexandria. Upon this, some of his rivals fraudulently bribed a jester who was attached to the court to carry him an invitation to dine with the king. Accordingly, Apelles attended; upon which Ptolemæus was highly indignant and, summoning before him his stewards of the household, requested that the artist would point out the one that had given him the invitation. Thus challenged, Apelles seized a piece of charcoal that lay in the fireplace and traced a likeness upon the wall with such exactness that the king, the moment he began it, recognized the features as those of the jester. He also painted a portrait of King Antigonus; and as that monarch was blind of one eye, he invented a method of concealing the defect. With this object, he painted him in profile, making it his care to show that side of the face only which he could show without any defect. Among his works there are some figures representing persons at the point of death; but it is not easy to say which of his productions are of the highest order of excellence.

His Venus Rising from the Sea, known as the Venus Anadyomene, was consecrated by the late Emperor Augustus in the Temple of his father Cæsar; a work which has been celebrated in certain Greek lines which, though they have outlived it, have perpetuated its fame. The lower part of the picture having become damaged, no one could be found to repair it; and thus did the very injury which the picture had sustained, redound to the glory of the artist.

There exists too, or did exist, a Horse that was painted by him for a pictorial contest; as to the merits of which

Apelles appealed from the judgment of his fellow men to that of the dumb quadrupeds. For, finding that by their intrigues his rivals were likely to get the better of him, he had some horses brought, and the picture of each artist successively shown to them. Accordingly, it was only at the sight of the horse painted by Apelles that they began to neigh; a thing that has always been the case since, whenever this test of his artistic skill has been employed.

His inventions in the art of painting have been highly serviceable to others; but one thing there was in which no one could imitate him. When his works were finished he used to cover them with a black varnish of such remarkable thinness that while by the reflection it gave more vivacity to the colors and preserved them from the contact of dust and dirt, its existence could only be detected by a person when close enough to touch it. In addition there was also this other great advantage attending it: the brightness of the colors was softened thereby and harmonized to the sight, looking as though they had been viewed from a distance and through a medium of specular stone; the contrivance, by some indescribable means, giving a somberness to colors which would otherwise have been too florid.

We must make some mention of those artists who acquired fame by the pencil in an inferior style of painting. Among these was Piræicus, inferior to few of the painters in skill. I am not sure that he did not do injustice to himself by the choice of his subjects, seeing that, although he adopted humble subjects, he still attained in that way the highest reputation. His subjects were barbers' shops, cobblers' stalls, jackasses, eatables, and the like, and to these he was indebted for his epithet of "Rhyparographos." His paintings are exquisitely pleasing, and have sold at higher prices than the very largest works of many masters.

On the other hand again, as Varro tells us, a single picture by Serapio covered the whole space of the balustrades beneath the Old Shops, where it was exhibited. This artist was very successful in painting stage scenery but was unable to depict the human form. Dionysius, on the contrary, painted nothing but men, and hence it was that he had the nickname of "Anthropographos."

It is said, that Pamphilus the instructor of Apelles not only painted in encaustic or wax, but also instructed Pausias of Sicyon in the art, the first who rendered himself distinguished in this branch. Pausias was the son of Bryetes, by whom he was originally instructed in the art of painting. He retouched with the pencil some walls at Thespiæ, then undergoing repair, which had formerly been painted by Polygnotus. It was he who first thought of painting ceilings; nor had it been the practice before his day to use this kind of decoration for arched roofs. He painted many small pictures also, miniatures of children more particularly; a thing which, according to the interpretation put upon it by his rivals, was owing to the peculiarly slow process of encaustic painting. The consequence was, that being determined to give a memorable proof of his celerity of execution, he completed a picture in the space of a single day, which was thence called the "Hemeresios," representing the portrait of a child.

In his youth he was enamored of Glycera, his fellow-townswoman, the first inventor of chaplets; and in his rivalry of the skill shown by her he achieved so much success in the encaustic art as to reproduce the almost numberless tints displayed by flowers.

Wax encaustic painting does not admit of being applied to walls, but is in common use by way of ornament for ships of war, and indeed merchant ships at the present day. As we go so far as to paint these vehicles of danger, no one can be surprised if we paint our funeral piles as well, or if we have our gladiators conveyed in handsome carriages to the scene of death, or of carnage. When we contemplate this extensive variety of color we cannot but admire the ingenuity displayed by the men of former days.

It was with four colors only that Apelles, Echion, Melanthius, and Nicomachus, those most illustrous paint-

ers, executed their immortal works; melinum for the white
Attic sil for the yellow, Pontic sinopis for the red, and atra
mentum for the black; and yet a single picture of theirs ha
sold before now for the treasures of whole cities. But at th
present day, when purple is employed for coloring wall
and when India sends to us the slime of her rivers and th
corrupt blood of her dragons and her elephants, there i
no such thing as a picture of high quality produced. Every
thing was superior at a time when the resources of art wer
so much fewer than they now are. Yes, so it is; and th
reason is that it is the material, and not the efforts of genius
that is now the object of research.

One folly of this age of ours, in reference to painting
I must not omit. The Emperor Nero ordered a painting o
himself to be executed upon canvas of colossal proportions
one hundred and twenty feet in height; a thing till the
unknown. This picture was just completed when it wa
burnt by lightning with the greater part of the gardens o
Maius in which it was exhibited.

A freedman of the same prince, on the occasion of hi
exhibiting a show of gladiators at Antium, had the publi
porticos hung with paintings in which were represente
genuine portraits of the gladiators and all the other as
sistants. Indeed at this place there has been a very prevail
ing taste for paintings for many ages past. C. Terentiu
Lucanus was the first who had combats of gladiators painte
for public exhibition: in honor of his grandfather who ha
adopted him, he provided thirty pairs of gladiators in th
Forum for three consecutive days, and exhibited a painting
of their combats in the Grove of Diana.

There have been some female painters also. Timaret
the daughter of Micon painted a Diana at Ephesus, on
of the very oldest panel paintings known. Irene, daughte
and pupil of the artist Cratinus, painted a figure of a girl
now at Eleusis, a Calypso, an Aged Man, the juggler Theo
dorus, and Alcisthenes the dancer. Aristarete, daughter an
pupil of Nearchus, painted an Æsculapius. Iaia of Cyzicus

who always remained single, painted at Rome in the youth of M. Varro, both with the brush, and with the graver, upon ivory, her subjects being female portraits mostly. At Naples there is a large picture by her, the portrait of an Old Woman; as also a portrait of herself taken by the aid of a mirror. There was no painter superior to her for expedition; while at the same time her artistic skill was such that her works sold at much higher prices than those of the most celebrated portrait painters of her day, Sopolis namely, and Dionysius, with whose pictures our galleries are filled. One Olympias painted also, but nothing is known relative to her except that she had Autobulus for a pupil.

In ancient times there were but two methods of encaustic painting, in wax and on ivory, with the cestrum or pointed graver. When this art came to be applied to the painting of ships of war a third method was adopted, that of melting the wax colors and laying them on with a brush while hot. Painting of this nature, applied to vessels, will never spoil from the action of the sun, winds, or salt water.

The Coloring of Cloth

In Egypt, too, they employ a very remarkable process for the coloring of cloth. After pressing the material, which is white at first, they saturate it, not with colors, but with mordents that are calculated to absorb color. This done, the cloths, still unchanged in appearance are plunged into a cauldron of boiling dye and are removed the next moment fully colored. It is a singular fact that although the dye in the pan is of one uniform color, the material when taken out of it is of various colors, according to the nature of the mordents that have been respectively applied to it: these colors will never wash out. Thus the dye pan, which under ordinary circumstances would have made but one color of several, if colored cloths had been put into it, is here made to yield several colors from a single dye. At the same moment that it dyes the cloths it boils in the color; and it is the fact that material which has been thus submitted to the action of fire becomes stouter and more serviceable for wear than it would have been if it had not been subjected to the process.

The Art of Modeling

On painting we have now said enough, and more than enough; but it will be only proper to append some accounts of the plastic art. Butades, a potter of Sicyon, was the first who invented, at Corinth, the art of modeling portraits in the earth which he used in his trade. It was through his daughter that he made the discovery; who being deeply in love with a young man about to depart on a long journey traced the profile of his face as thrown upon the wall by the light of the lamp. Upon seeing this, her father filled in the outline by compressing clay upon the surface, and so made a face in relief which he then hardened by fire along with other articles of pottery. This model, it is said, was preserved in the Nymphæum at Corinth until the destruction of that city by Mummius. Others assert that the first inventors of the plastic art were Rhœcus and Theodorus at Samos, a considerable period before the expulsion of the Bacchiadæ from Corinth; and that Damaratus, on taking to flight from that place and settling in Etruria where he became father of Tarquinius, who was ultimately king of the Roman people, was accompanied by the modelers Euchir, Diopus, and Eugrammus, by whose agency the art was first introduced into Italy.

Butades first invented the method of coloring plastic compositions, by adding red earth to the material, or else modeling them in red clay: he too was the first to make masks on the outer edges of gutter tiles upon the roofs of buildings, in low relief, and known as "prostypa" at first, but afterwards in high relief or "ectypa." It was in these designs that the ornaments on the pediments of temples originated; and from this invention modelers first had their name of "plastæ."

The first person who reproduced the human features by fitting a mold of plaster upon the face and then pouring melted wax into the cast was Lysistratus of Sicyon, brother of Lysippus. It was he who first made it his study to give a faithful likeness; for before his time artists only thought how to make their portraits as handsome as possible. The same artist was the first who thought of making models for his statues; a method which afterwards became so universally adopted that there could be neither figure nor statue made without its model in clay. Hence it would appear that the art of modeling in clay is more ancient than that of molding in bronze.

The most celebrated modelers were Damophilus and Gorgasus, who were painters as well. These artists adorned with their works in both kinds the Temple of Ceres in the Circus Maximus at Rome; with an inscription in Greek which stated that the decorations on the right hand were the workmanship of Damophilus, and those on the left, of Gorgasus. Varro says that before the construction of this temple everything was Tuscan in the temples; and that when the temple was afterwards repaired the painted coatings of the walls were cut away in tablets and enclosed in frames, but that the figures on the pediments were dispersed. Chalcosthenes executed at Athens some works in unbaked earth on the spot which from his manufactory has since obtained the name of "Ceramicus."

M. Varro states that he knew an artist at Rome, Possis by name, who executed fruit, grapes, and fish with such exactness that it was quite impossible, by only looking at them, to distinguish them from the reality.

Varro praises Pasiteles also, who used to say that the plastic art was the mother of chasing, statuary, and sculpture, and who, excellent as he was in each of these branches, never executed any work without first modeling it. In addition to these particulars he states that the art of modeling was anciently cultivated in Italy, Etruria in particular, and that Volcanius was summoned from Veii and entrusted by Tarquinius Priscus with making the figure of Jupiter, which he intended to consecrate in the Capitol; that this Jupiter was made of clay, and that hence arose the custom of painting it with minium; and that the four-horse chariot, so often mentioned, upon the pediment of the temple, was made of clay as well.

Works in Poetry

Statues of this nature are still in existence at various places. At Rome and in our municipal towns we still see many such pediments of temples; wonderful too for their workmanship, and from their artistic merit and long duration more deserving of our respect than gold, and certainly far less baneful. At the present day, in the midst of such wealth as we possess, we make our first libation at the sacrifice, not from murrhine vases or vessels of crystal but from ladles made of earthenware.

Bounteous beyond expression is the earth, if we only consider in detail her various gifts. To omit all mention of the cereals, wine, fruits, herbs, shrubs, medicaments, and metals, bounties which she has lavished upon us, and which have already passed under our notice, her productions in the shape of pottery alone would more than suffice in their variety to satisfy our domestic wants; what with gutter tiles of earthenware, vats for receiving wine, pipes for conveying water, conduits for supplying baths, baked tiles for roofs, bricks for foundations, the productions, too, of the potter's wheel; results, all of them, of an art, which induced King Numa to establish, as a seventh company, the makers of earthenware.

Even more than this, many persons have chosen to be

buried in coffins made of earthenware; M. Varro for instance, who was interred, in true Pythagorean style, in the midst of leaves of myrtle, olive, and black poplar; indeed, the greater part of mankind make use of earthen vases for this purpose. For the service of the table, the Samian pottery is even yet held in high esteem; that too of Arretium in Italy still maintains its high character; while for their cups, and for those only, the manufactories of Surrentum, Asta, Pollentia, Saguntum in Spain, and Pergamus in Asia, are greatly esteemed.

The city of Tralles in Asia, and that of Mutina in Italy, have their respective manufactures of earthenware, and even by this branch of art are localities rendered famous; their productions, by the aid of the potter's wheel, becoming known to all countries and conveyed by sea and by land to every quarter of the earth. At Erythræ there are still shown in a temple there two amphoræ that were consecrated in consequence of the singular thinness of the material: they originated in a contest between a master and his pupil, which of the two could make earthenware of the greatest thinness. The vessels of Cos are the most highly celebrated for their beauty, but those of Adria are considered the most substantial.

Vitellius, when emperor, ordered a dish to be made which was to cost a million of sesterces and for the preparation of which a furnace had to be erected out in the fields! luxury having thus arrived at such a pitch of excess as to make earthenware sell at higher prices than murrhine vessels. It was in reference to this circumstance that Mucianus in his second consulship, when pronouncing one of his perorations, reproached the memory of Vitellius with his dishes as broad as the Pomptine Marsh.

What is there that human industry will not devise? Even broken pottery has been utilized; it being found that, beaten to powder and tempered with lime, it becomes more solid and durable than other substances of a similar nature, forming the cement known as the "Signine" composition, so extensively employed for making the pavements of houses.

The art of modeling was prior to that of statuary. This last, however, has flourished to such an extraordinary degree that an account of it would fill many volumes if we were desirous of making an extensive acquaintance with the subject: but as to learning everything connected with it, who could do it?

Sculpture

In the ædileship of M. Scaurus, there were three thousand statues erected on the stage of what was a temporary theater only. Mummius the conqueror of Achaia filled the City with statues; he who at his death was destined not to leave a dowry to his daughter. The Luculli also introduced many articles from abroad. Yet we learn from Mucianus, who was thrice consul, that there are still three thousand statues in Rhodes, and it is supposed that there are no fewer in existence at Athens, at Olympia, and at Delphi. What living mortal could enumerate them all? or of what utility would be such information? Still I may perhaps afford amusement by giving some slight account of such of those works of art as are in any way remarkable, and stating the names of the more celebrated artists. Of each of these it would be impossible to enumerate all the productions, for Lysippus alone is said to have executed no less than fifteen hundred works of art, all of which were of such excellence that any one of them might have immortalized him. The number was ascertained by his heir upon opening his coffers after his death, it having been his practice to lay up one golden denarius out of the sum which he had received as the price of each statue.

This art has arrived at incredible perfection, both in successfulness and in boldness of design. As a proof of successfulness I will adduce one example, and that of a figure which represented neither god nor man. We have seen in our own time in the Capitol, before it was last burnt by the party of Vitellius, in the shrine of Juno there, a bronze figure of a dog licking its wounds. Its miraculous excellence and its perfect truthfulness were not only proved by the circumstance of its having been consecrated there but also by the novel kind of security that was taken for its safety; for, no sum appearing equal to its value, it was publicly enacted that the keepers of it should be answerable for its safety with their lives.

Colossal Statues

As to boldness of design, the examples are innumerable; for we see statues of enormous bulk, known as colossal statues and equal to towers in size. Such for instance is the Apollo in the Capitol, which was brought by M. Lucullus from Apollonia a city of Pontus, thirty cubits in height, and which cost five hundred talents: such, too, is the statue of Jupiter in the Campus Martius, dedicated by the late Emperor Claudius, but which appears small in comparison from its vicinity to the Theater of Pompeius: and such is that at Tarentum, forty cubits in height, and the work of Lysippus. It is a remarkable circumstance in this statue that though, as it is stated, it is so nicely balanced as to be movable by the hand it has never been thrown down by a tempest. This indeed the artist, it is said, has guarded against by a column erected at a short distance from it upon the side on which the violence of the wind had to be broken. On account of its magnitude and the great difficulty of moving it, Fabius Verrucosus did not touch it when he transferred the Hercules from that place to the Capitol, where it now stands.

But that which is by far the most worthy of our admiration is the colossal statue of the Sun which stood formerly at Rhodes and was the work of Chares the Lindian, a pupil of the above-named Lysippus; no less than seventy cubits in height. This statue, fifty-six years after it was erected was thrown down by an earthquake; but even as it lies it excites our wonder and admiration. Few men can clasp the thumb in their arms and its fingers are larger than most statues. Where the limbs are broken asunder vast caverns are seen yawning in the interior. Within it, too, are to be seen large masses of rock, by the weight of which the artist steadied it while erecting it. It is said that it was twelve years before this statue was completed and that three hundred talents were expended upon it; a sum raised from the engines of warfare which had been abandoned by King Demetrius when tired of the long-protracted siege of Rhodes. In the same city there are other colossal statues, one hundred in number; but though smaller than the one already mentioned, wherever erected, they would, any one of them, have ennobled the place. In addition to these there are five colossal statues of the gods, which were made by Bryaxis.

Colossal statues used also to be made in Italy. At all events we see the Tuscan Apollo, in the library of the Temple of Augustus, fifty feet in height from the toe; and it is a question whether it is more remarkable for the quality of the metal or for the beauty of the workmanship. Spurius Carvilius also erected the statue of Jupiter which is seen in the Capitol, after he had conquered the Samnites, who fought in obedience to a most solemn oath; it being formed out of their breastplates, greaves, and helmets, and of such large dimensions that it may be seen from the statue of Jupiter Latiaris. He made his own statue, which is at the feet of the other one, out of the filings of the metal.

But all these gigantic statues of this kind have been surpassed in our own age by that of Mercury, made by Zenodotus for the city of the Arverni in Gaul, which was ten years in being completed, and the making of which cost four hundred thousand sesterces. Having given sufficient proof there of his artistic skill, he was sent for by

Nero to Rome where he made a colossal statue intended to represent that prince, one hundred and ten feet in height. In consequence of the public detestation of Nero's crimes, this statue was consecrated to the Sun. We used to admire in his studio, not only the accurate likeness in the model of clay, but the small sketches also which served as the first foundation of the work.

Among all nations which the fame of the Olympian Jupiter has reached, Phidias is looked upon, beyond all doubt, as the most famous of artists: but to let those who have never even seen his works know how deservedly he is esteemed we will take this opportunity of adducing a few slight proofs of the genius which he displayed. In doing this we shall not appeal to the beauty of his Olympian Jupiter, nor yet to the vast proportions of his Athenian Minerva, six and twenty cubits in height and composed of ivory and gold; but it is to the shield of this last statue that we shall draw attention; upon the convex face of which he has chased a combat of the Amazons, while, upon the concave side of it he has represented the battle between the Gods and the Giants. Upon the sandals we see the wars of the Lapithæ and Centaurs, so careful has he been to fill every smallest portion of his work with some proof or other of his artistic skill. To the story chased upon the pedestal of the statue the name of the "Birth of Pandora" has been given; and the figures of newborn gods to be seen upon it are no less than twenty in number. The figure of Victory in particular is most admirable, and connoisseurs are greatly struck with the serpent and the sphinx in bronze lying beneath the point of the spear. Let thus much be said incidentally in reference to an artist who can never be sufficiently praised; if only to let it be understood that the richness of his genius was always equal to itself, even in the very smallest details.

Praxiteles was an artist who, in the glory which he acquired by his works in marble, surpassed even himself. There are some works of his in the Ceramicus at Athens;

but, superior to all statues, not only by Praxiteles but by any other artist that ever existed is his Cnidian Venus; for the inspection of which many persons before now have purposely undertaken a voyage to Cnidos. The artist made two statues of the goddess and offered them both for sale: one of them was represented with drapery, and for this reason was preferred by the people of Cos, who had the choice; the second was offered them at the same price but, on the grounds of propriety and modesty, they thought fit to choose the other. Upon this, the Cnidians purchased the rejected statue, and immensely superior has it always been held in general estimation. At a later period King Nicomedes wished to purchase this statue of the Cnidians and made them an offer to pay off the whole of their public debt, which was very large. They preferred, however, to submit to any extremity rather than part with it; and with good reason, for by this statue Praxiteles has perpetuated the glory of Cnidos.

Small Works

Callicrates used to carve ants and other small animals in ivory, so minute in size that other persons were unable to distinguish their individual parts. Myrmecides also was famous in the same line; this man made, of similar material, a chariot drawn by four horses, which a fly could cover with its wings; as well as a ship which might be covered by the wings of a tiny bee.

Marble

M. Lepidus, who was consul with Q. Catulus, was the first to have the lintels of his house made of Numidian marble, a thing for which he was greatly censured: he was consul in the year of Rome, 676. This is the earliest instance that I can find of the introduction of Numidian marble; not in the form of pillars or of slabs, as was the case with the marble of Carystus, but in blocks, and that too for the comparatively ignoble purpose of making the thresholds of doors. Four years after this Lepidus, L. Lucullus was consul; the same person who gave its name, it is very evident, to the Lucullan marble; for, taking a great fancy to it, he introduced it at Rome. While other kinds of marble are valued for their spots or their colors, this marble is entirely black. It is found in the island of Melos and is pretty nearly the only marble that has taken its name from the person who first introduced it. Among these personages, Scaurus, in my opinion was the first to build a theater with walls of marble: but whether they were only coated with slabs of marble or were made of solid blocks highly polished such as we now see in the Temple of Jupiter Tonans in the Capitol, I cannot exactly say: for up to this period I cannot find any vestiges of the use of marble slabs in Italy.

But whoever it was that first invented the art of cutting marble and so multiplying the appliances of luxury, he displayed considerable ingenuity, though to little purpose. This division, though apparently effected by the aid of iron, is in reality effected by sand; the saw acting only by pressing upon the sand within a very fine cleft in the stone as it is moved to and fro.

The sand of Ethiopia is the most highly esteemed for this purpose; for, to add to the trouble that is entailed, we have to send to Ethiopia for the purpose of preparing our marble—aye, and as far as India even; whereas in former times the Romans thought it beneath them to repair thither in search of such costly things even as pearls! This Indian sand is held in the next highest degree of estimation, the Ethiopian being of a softer nature and better adapted for dividing the stone without leaving any roughness on the surface; whereas the sand from India does not leave so smooth a face upon it. Still, for polishing marble, we find it recommended to rub it with Indian sand calcined. The sand of Naxos has the same defect; as also that from Coptos, generally known as "Egyptian" sand.

The above were the several varieties of sand used by the ancients in dividing marble. More recently a sand has been discovered that is equally approved of for this purpose; in a certain creek of the Adriatic Sea, which is left dry at low water only; a thing that renders it not very easy to be found. At the present day, however, the fraudulent tendencies of our workers in marble have emboldened them to use any kind of river sand for the purpose; a mischief which very few employers rightly appreciate. For the coarser the sand the wider is the division made in the stone, the greater the quantity of material consumed, and the more extensive the labor required for polishing the rough surface that is left; a result of which is that the slabs lose so much more in thickness. For giving the last polish to marble, Thebaic stone is considered well adapted, as also porous stone, or pumice, powdered fine.

Obelisks

Monarchs have entered into a sort of rivalry with one another in forming elongated blocks of stone known as "obelisks" and consecrated to the divinity of the Sun. The blocks had this form given to them in resemblance to the rays of that luminary, which are so called in the Egyptian language.

Mesphres who reigned in the City of the Sun was the first who erected one of these obelisks, being warned to do so in a dream: indeed there is an inscription upon the obelisk to this effect; for the sculptures and figures which we still see engraved thereon are no other than Egyptian letters.

At a later period other kings had these obelisks hewn. Sesosthes erected four of them in the above-named city, forty-eight cubits in height. Rhamsesis, too, who was reigning at the time of the capture of Troy, erected one a hundred and forty cubits high. Having quitted the spot where the palace of Mnevis stood, this monarch erected another obelisk one hundred and twenty cubits in height, but of prodigious thickness, the sides being no less than eleven cubits in breadth. It is said that one hundred and twenty thousand men were employed upon this work; and that the king, when it was on the point of being elevated, being apprehensive that the machinery employed might not prove strong enough for the weight, with the view of increasing the peril that might be entailed by due want of precaution on the part of the workmen, had his own son fastened to the summit; in order that the safety of the prince might at the same time insure the safety of the mass of stone. It was in his admiration of this work that, when King Cambyses took the city by storm and the conflagration had already reached the very foot of the obelisk, he ordered the fire to be extinguished; he entertaining a respect for this stupendous erection which he had not entertained for the city itself.

There are also two other obelisks, one of them erected by Zmarres and the other by Phius, both of them without inscriptions and forty-eight cubits in height. Ptolemæus Philadelphus had one erected at Alexandria, eighty cubits high, which had been prepared by order of King Necthebis: it was without any inscription and cost far more trouble in its carriage and elevation than had been originally expended in quarrying it. Some writers inform us that it was conveyed on a raft under the inspection of the architect Satyrus; but Callixenus gives the name of Phœnix. For this purpose a canal was dug from the river Nile to the spot where the obelisk lay; and two broad vessels laden with blocks of similar stone a foot square, the cargo of each amounting to double the size and consequently double the weight of the obelisk, were brought beneath it; the extremities of the obelisk remaining supported by the opposite sides of the canal. The blocks of stone were then removed and the vessels, being thus gradually lightened, received their burden. It was erected upon a basis of six square blocks, quarried from the same mountain, and the artist was rewarded with the sum of fifty talents. This obelisk was placed by the king above-mentioned in the Arsinœum in testimony of his affection for his wife and sister Arsinoë. At a later period, as it was found to be an inconvenience to the docks, Maximus the then præfect of Egypt had it transferred to the Forum there, after removing the summit for the purpose of substituting a gilded point; an intention which was ultimately abandoned.

There are two other obelisks, which were in Cæsar's Temple at Alexandria near the harbor, forty-two cubits in height and originally hewn by order of King Mesphres. But the most difficult enterprise of all was the carriage of these obelisks by sea to Rome in vessels which excited the greatest admiration. Indeed the late Emperor Augustus consecrated the one which brought over the first obelisk as a lasting memorial of this marvelous undertaking, in the docks at Puteoli; but it was destroyed by fire. As to the one in which, by order of the Emperor Caius, the other obelisk had been transported to Rome, after having been preserved for some years and looked upon as the most wonderful ship ever beheld upon the seas, it was brought to Ostia by order of the late Emperor Claudius; and towers of Puteolan earth being first erected upon it, it was sunk for the construction of the harbor which he was making there. And then, besides, there was the necessity of constructing other vessels to carry these obelisks up the Tiber; by which it became practically ascertained, that the depth of water in that river is not less than that of the river Nile.

The obelisk that was erected by the late Emperor Augustus in the Circus Maximus was originally quarried by order of King Semenpserteus, in whose reign it was that Pythagoras visited Egypt. It is eighty-five feet and three quarters in height, exclusive of the base which is a part of the same stone. The one that he erected in the

Campus Martius is nine feet less in height and was originally made by order of Sesothis. They are both of them covered with inscriptions which interpret the operations of Nature according to the philosophy of the Egyptians.

The one erected in the Campus Martius has been applied to a singular purpose by the late Emperor Augustus; that of marking the shadows projected by the sun and so measuring the length of the days and nights. With this object, a stone pavement was laid, the extreme length of which corresponded exactly with the length of the shadow thrown by the obelisk at the sixth hour on the day of the winter solstice. After this period the shadow would go on, day by day, gradually decreasing, and then again would as gradually increase, corresponding with certain lines of brass that were inserted in the stone; a device well deserving to be known, and due to the ingenuity of Facundus Novus, the mathematician.

Section XVI
MINERALS

Gold

The first great proof of the goodness of gold is its high melting point; in addition to which it is a fact truly marvelous, that, though proof against the most intense fire if made with wood charcoal, it will melt with the greatest readiness upon a fire made with chaff; and that, for the purpose of purifying it, it is fused with lead. There is another reason too, which still more tends to enhance its value, the fact that it wears off the least of all metals by continual use: whereas with silver, copper, and lead the hands become soiled with the substance that comes from off them. Nor is there any material more malleable than this, none that admits of a more extended division, seeing that a single ounce of it admits of being beaten out into seven hundred and fifty leaves or more, four fingers in length by the same in breadth. The thickest kind of gold leaf is known as "leaf of Præneste," it still retaining that name from the excellence of the gilding upon the statue of Fortune there. The next in thickness is known as the "quæstorian leaf."

Gold is the only metal found pure in masses or in the form of dust; and whereas all other metals, when found in the ore, require to be purified by the aid of fire, this gold that I am speaking of is gold the moment it is found and has all its component parts already in a state of perfection. This, however, is only such gold as is found in the native state, the other kinds being refined by art. And then, more than anything else, gold is subject to no rust, no verdigris, no emanation whatever from it, either to alter its quality or to lessen its weight. In addition to this, gold steadily resists the corrosive action of salt and vinegar, things which obtain the mastery over all other substances: it admits beyond all other metals of being spun out and woven like wool. Verrius tells us that Tarquinius Priscus celebrated a triumph clad in a tunic of gold; and I myself have seen Agrippina the wife of the Emperor Claudius, on the occasion of a naval combat which he exhibited, seated by him attired in a military scarf made entirely of woven gold without any other material. For this long time past, gold has been interwoven in the Attalic textures, an invention of the kings of Asia.

Gilding

On marble and other substances which do not admit of being brought to a white heat, gilt is laid with glair of egg, and on wood by the aid of a glutinous composition.

The most convenient method for gilding copper would be to employ quicksilver. To effect this mode of gilding, the copper is first well hammered, after which it is subjected to the action of fire, and then cooled with a mixture of salt, vinegar, and alum. It is then cleansed of all extraneous substances, its brightness indicating when it has been sufficiently purified. This done, it is again heated by fire in order to enable it, when prepared with an amalgam of pumice, alum, and quicksilver, to receive the gold leaf.

How Gold Is Found

Gold is found in our own part of the world; not to mention the gold extracted from the earth in India by the ants, and in Scythia by the Griffins. Among us it is procured in three different ways; the first of which is in the shape of dust found in running streams, the Tagus in Spain, for instance, the Padus in Italy, the Hebrus in Thracia, the Pactolus in Asia, and the Ganges in India; indeed there is no gold found in a more perfect state than this, thoroughly polished as it is by the continual attrition of the current.

A second mode of obtaining gold is by sinking shafts or seeking it among the debris of mountains. The persons in search of gold in the first place remove the "segutilum," this being the name of the earth which gives indication of the presence of gold. This done, a bed is made, the sand of which is washed, and, according to the residue found after washing, a conjecture is formed as to the richness of the vein. Sometimes gold is found in the surface earth, a success but rarely experienced. Recently, in the reign of Nero, a vein was discovered in Dalmatia, which yielded daily as much as fifty pounds' weight of gold. The gold that is thus found in the surface crust is known as "talutium," in cases where there is auriferous earth beneath. The mountains of Spain, in other respects arid and sterile and productive of nothing whatever, are thus constrained by man to be fertile in supplying him with this precious commodity.

The gold that is extracted from shafts is known by some persons as "canalicium," and by others as "canaliense"; it is found adhering to the gritty crust of marble and, altogether different from the form in which it sparkles in the sapphirus of the East and in the stone of Thebais and other gems, it is seen interlaced with the molecules of the marble. The channels of these veins are found running in various directions along the sides of the shafts. In these shafts the earth is kept from falling in by means of wooden pillars. The substance that is extracted is first broken up and then washed; after which it is subjected to the action of fire, and ground to a fine powder. The impurities that escape by the chimney, as with all other metals, are known by the name of "scoria." In the case of gold, this scoria is broken up a second time and melted over again. The crucibles used for this purpose are made of "tasconium," a white earth similar to potter's clay in appearance; there being no other substance capable of withstanding the strong current of air, the action of the fire, and the intense heat of the melted metal.

The third method of obtaining gold surpasses the labors of the Giants: by the aid of galleries driven to a long distance, mountains are excavated by the light of torches, the duration of which forms the set times for work, the workmen never seeing the light of day for many months together. These mines are known as "arrugiæ"; and frequently clefts are formed on a sudden, the earth sinks in, and the workmen are crushed beneath; so that it would really appear less rash to go in search of pearls and purples at the bottom of the sea, so much more dangerous to ourselves have we made the earth than the water! Hence it is that in this kind of mining arches are left at frequent intervals for the purpose of supporting the weight of the mountain above. In mining either by shaft or by gallery barriers of silex are met with, which have to be driven asunder by the aid of fire and vinegar; or more frequently, as this method fills the galleries with suffocating vapors and smoke, to be broken to pieces with bruising-machines shod with pieces of iron weighing one hundred and fifty pounds: which done, the fragments are carried out on the workmen's shoulders, night and day, each man passing them on to his neighbor in the dark, it being only those at the pit's mouth that ever see the light. In cases where the bed of silex appears too thick to admit of being penetrated, the miner traces along the sides of it and so turns it. And yet the labor entailed by this silex is looked upon as comparatively easy, there being an earth—a kind of potter's clay mixed with gravel, "gangadia" by name, which it is almost impossible to overcome. This earth has to be attacked with iron wedges and hammers and it is generally considered that there is nothing more stubborn in existence —except indeed the greed for gold, which is the most stubborn of all things.

When these operations are completed, beginning at

the last they cut away the wooden pillars at the point
where they support the roof: the coming downfall gives
warning which is instantly perceived by the sentinel, and
by him only who is set to watch upon a peak of the same
mountain. By voice as well as by signals he orders the
workmen to be immediately summoned from their labors
and at the same moment takes to flight himself. The mountain, rent to pieces, is cleft asunder, hurling its debris to a
distance with a crash which it is impossible for the human
imagination to conceive; and from the midst of a cloud of
dust of a density quite incredible the victorious miners
gaze upon this downfall of Nature. Nor yet even then are
they sure of gold, nor indeed were they by any means certain that there was any to be found when they first began
to excavate, it being quite sufficient as an inducement to
undergo such perils and to incur such vast expense, to entertain the hope that they shall obtain what they so eagerly
desire.

Another labor quite equal to this, and one which en-
tails even greater expense, is that of bringing rivers from
the more elevated mountain heights, a distance in many instances of one hundred miles, for the purpose of washing
these debris. The channels thus formed are called "cor-
rugi," from our word "corrivatio," I suppose; and even
when these are once made they entail a thousand fresh
labors. The fall, for instance, must be steep that the water
may be precipitated, so to say, rather than flow; and it is
in this manner that it is brought from the most elevated
points. Then, too, valleys and crevasses have to be united
by the aid of aqueducts, and in another place impassable
rocks have to be hewn away and forced to make room for
hollowed troughs of wood; the person hewing them hanging suspended all the time with ropes, so that to a spectator who views the operations from a distance the workmen have all the appearance, not so much of wild beasts, as
of birds upon the wing. Hanging thus they take the levels
and trace with lines the course the water is to take; and

thus, where there is no room even for man to plant a footstep, are rivers traced out by the hand of man. The water is considered in an unfit state for washing if the current of the river carries any mud along with it. The kind of earth that yields this mud is known as "urium"; and hence it is that in tracing out these channels they carry the water over beds of silex or pebbles, and carefully avoid this urium. When they have reached the head of the fall, at the very brow of the mountain reservoirs are hollowed out a couple of hundred feet in length and breadth and some ten feet in depth. In these reservoirs there are generally five sluices left, about three feet square; so that the moment the reservoir is filled the floodgates are struck away and the torrent bursts forth with such a degree of violence as to roll onwards any fragments of rock which may obstruct its passage.

When they have reached the level ground there is still another labor that awaits them. Trenches—known as "agogæ"—have to be dug for the passage of the water; and these, at regular intervals, have a layer of ulex placed at the bottom. This ulex is a plant like rosemary in appearance, rough and prickly and well adapted for arresting any pieces of gold that may be carried along. The sides are closed in with planks, and are supported by arches when carried over steep and precipitous spots. The earth carried onwards in the stream arrives at the sea at last, and thus is the shattered mountain washed away; causes which have greatly tended to extend the shores of Spain by these encroachments upon the deep. It is also by the agency of canals of this description that the material excavated at the cost of such immense labor by the process previously described is washed and carried away; for otherwise the shafts would soon be choked up by it.

The gold found by excavating with galleries does not require to be melted, but is pure gold at once. In these excavations it is found in lumps, as also in the shafts which are sunk, sometimes exceeding ten pounds. The names given to these lumps are "palagæ," and "palacurnæ," while the gold found in small grains is known as "baluce." The ulex that is used for the above purpose is dried and burnt, after which the ashes of it are washed upon a bed of grassy turf in order that the gold may be deposited thereupon.

Asturia, Gallæcia, and Lusitania furnish in this manner yearly, according to some authorities, twenty thousand pounds' weight of gold, the produce of Asturia forming the major part. Indeed there is no part of the world that for centuries has maintained such a continuous fertility in gold. In abundance of metals of every kind Italy yields to no land whatever; but all search for them has been prohibited by an ancient decree of the Senate, who gave orders thereby that Italy shall be exempt from such treatment.

Silver

There are two kinds of silver. On placing a piece of it upon an iron fire shovel at a white heat, if the metal remains perfectly white it is of the best quality: if it turns of a reddish color it is inferior; but if it becomes black it is worthless. Fraud, however, has devised means of stultifying this test; for by keeping the shovel immersed in men's urine, the piece of silver absorbs it as it burns, and so displays a fictitious whiteness. There is also a kind of test with reference to polished silver: when the human breath comes in contact with it, it should immediately be covered with steam, the cloudiness disappearing at once.

Mirrors

It is generally supposed among us that it is only the very finest silver that admits of being laminated and so converted into mirrors. Pure silver was formerly used for the purpose, but at the present day this too has been corrupted by fraud. But, really, it is a very marvelous property that this metal has of reflecting objects; a property which, it is generally agreed, results from the repercussion of the air, thrown back as it is from the metal upon the eyes. The same too is the action that takes place when we use a mirror. If a thick plate of this metal is highly polished and is rendered slightly concave the image or object reflected is enlarged to an immense extent; so vast is the difference between a surface receiving, and throwing back the air. Even more—drinking cups are now made in such a manner as to be filled inside with numerous concave facets, like so many mirrors; so that if one person looks into the interior he sees reflected a whole multitude of persons.

Mirrors have been invented to reflect monstrous forms; those for instance, which have been consecrated in the Temple at Smyrna. This results from the configuration given to the metal; and it makes all the difference whether the surface has a concave form like the section of a drinking cup, or whether it is convex like a Thracian buckler; whether it is depressed in the middle or elevated; whether the surface has a direction transversely or obliquely; or whether it runs horizontally or vertically; the peculiar configuration of the surface which receives the shadows causing them to undergo corresponding distortions: for the image is nothing else but the shadow of the object collected upon the bright surface of the metal.

However, to finish our description of mirrors—the best in the times of our ancestors were those of Brundisium, composed of a mixture of stannum and copper: at a later period those made of silver were preferred, Pasiteles being the first who made them, in the time of Pompeius Magnus. More recently a notion has arisen that the object is reflected with greater distinctness by the application to the back of the mirror of a layer of gold.

Quicksilver

There is a mineral also found in these veins of silver which yields a humor that is always liquid and is known as "quicksilver." It acts as a poison upon everything, and pierces vessels, making its way through them by the agency of its malignant properties. All substances float upon the surface of quicksilver, with the exception of gold, this being the only substance that it attracts to itself. Hence it is that it is such an excellent refiner of gold; for on being briskly shaken in an earthen vessel with gold it rejects all the impurities that are mixed with it. When once it has thus expelled these superfluities there is nothing to do but to separate it from the gold; to effect which it is poured out upon skins that have been well tawed, and so exuding through them like a sort of perspiration, it leaves the gold in a state of purity behind.

Hence it is that when copper has to be gilded a coat of quicksilver is laid beneath the gold leaf, which it retains in its place with the greatest tenacity: in cases where the leaf is single or very thin the presence of the quicksilver is detected by the paleness of the color. For this reason, persons meditating a piece of fraud have been in the habit of substituting glair of egg for quicksilver, and then laying upon it a coat of hydrargyros. Generally speaking, quicksilver has not been found in any large quantities.

Copper

In Cyprian copper we have the kind known as "coronarium," and that called "regulare," both of them ductile. The former is made into thin leaves and, after being colored with ox-gall, is used for what has all the appearance of gilding on the coronets worn upon the stage. The same substance, if mixed with gold in the proportion of six scruples of gold to the ounce, and reduced into thin plates, acquires a fiery red color, and is termed "pyropus." In other mines they prepare the kind known as "regulare," as also that which is called "caldarium." These differ from each other in this respect, that in the latter the metal is only fused and breaks when struck with the hammer, whereas the "regulare" is malleable, or ductile as some call it, a property which belongs naturally to all the copper of Cyprus. In the case of all the other mines this difference between bar copper and cast brass is produced by artificial means. All the ores, in fact, will produce bar or malleable copper when sufficiently melted and purified by heat. Among the other kinds of copper, the palm of excellence is awarded to that of Campania which is the most esteemed for vessels and utensils. This last is prepared several ways. At Capua it is melted upon fires made with wood, and not coals, after which it is sprinkled with cold water and cleansed through a sieve made of oak. After being thus smelted a number of times, Spanish silver lead is added to it in the proportion of ten pounds of lead to one hundred pounds of copper; a method by which it is rendered pliable, and made to assume that agreeable color which is imparted to other kinds of copper by the application of oil and the action of the sun. Many parts of Italy and the provinces produce a similar kind of metal; but there they add only eight pounds of lead and, in consequence of the scarcity of wood, melt it several times over upon coals. It is in Gaul more particularly, where the ore is melted between red-hot stones, that the difference is to be seen that is produced by these variations in the method of smelting. Indeed this last method scorches the metal and renders it black and friable. Besides, they only melt it twice; whereas the oftener this operation is repeated the better in quality it becomes.

It is also as well to remark that all copper fuses best when the weather is intensely cold. The proper combination for making statues and tablets is as follows: the ore is first melted; after which there is added to the molten metal one third part of second-hand copper, or in other words, copper that has been in use and bought up for the purpose. For it is a peculiarity of this metal that when it has been some time in use and has been subject to long-continued friction it becomes seasoned and subdued, as it were, to a high polish. Twelve pounds and a half of silver lead are then added to every hundred pounds of fused metal.

The Metal Called Live Iron

We shall speak of the loadstone and of the sympathy which it has with iron. This is the only metal that acquires the properties of that stone, retaining them for a length of time and attracting other iron, so that we may sometimes see a whole chain formed of these rings. The lower classes in their ignorance call this "live iron," and the wounds that are made by it are much more severe. This mineral is also found in Cantabria, not in continuous strata like the genuine loadstone, but in scattered fragments which they call "bullationes." I do not know whether this species of ore is proper also for the fusion of glass, as no one has hitherto tried it; but it certainly imparts the same property as the magnet to iron. The architect Timochares began to erect a vaulted roof of loadstone in the Temple of Arsinoë at Alexandria, in order that the iron statue of that princess might have the appearance of hanging suspended in the air: his death, and that of King Ptolemæus who had ordered this monument to be erected in honor of his sister, prevented the completion of the project.

Plated Ware

It was in the Gallic provinces that the method was discovered of coating articles of copper with white lead, so as to be scarcely distinguishable from silver: articles thus plated are known as "incoctilia." At a later period the people of the town of Alesia began to use a similar process for plating articles with silver, more particularly ornaments for horses, beasts of burden, and yokes of oxen: the merit, however, of this invention belongs to the Bituriges. After this they began to ornament their esseda, colisata, and petorita in a similar manner; and luxury has at last arrived at such a pitch, that not only are their decorations made of silver, but of gold even, and what was formerly a marvel to behold on a cup is now subjected to the wear and tear of a carriage, and this in obedience to what they call fashion!

White lead is tested by pouring it, melted, upon paper, which ought to have the appearance of being torn rather by the weight than by the heat of the metal. India has neither copper nor lead, but she procures them in exchange for her precious stones and pearls.

Bitumen

Nearly approaching to the nature of sulphur is that of bitumen, which in some places assumes the form of a slime, and in others that of an earth; a slime thrown up by a certain lake in Judæa, and an earth found in the vicinity of Sidon, a maritime town of Syria. In both these states it admits of being thickened and condensed. There is also a liquid bitumen, that of Zacynthus, for example, and the bitumen that is imported from Babylon; which last kind is also white: the bitumen, too, of Apollonia is liquid. All these kinds have the one general name of "pissasphaltos," from their strong resemblance to a compound of pitch and bitumen. There is also found an unctuous liquid bitumen, resembling oil, in a spring at Agrigentum in Sicily, the waters of which are tainted by it. The inhabitants of the spot collect it on the panicles of reeds, to which it very readily adheres, and make use of it for burning in lamps as a substitute for oil, as also for the cure of itch scab in beasts of burden.

Bitumen to be of good quality should be extremely brilliant, heavy, and massive; it should also be moderately smooth, it being very much the practice to adulterate it with pitch. Its medicinal properties are similar to those of sulphur, it being naturally astringent, dispersive, contractive, and agglutinating: ignited, it drives away serpents by the smell. Babylonian bitumen is very efficacious, it is said, for the cure of cataract and albugo, as also of leprosy, lichens, and pruriginous affections.

Another use that is made of it is for coating the inside of copper vessels, it rendering them proof against the action of fire. Bitumen was formerly employed for staining copper and coating statues. It has been used as a substitute for lime; the walls of Babylon, for instance, are cemented with it. In the smithies they are in the habit of varnishing iron and heads of nails with it, and of using it for many other purposes as well.

In Samosata, a city of Commagene, there is a pool which discharges an inflammable mud called Maltha. It adheres to every solid body which it touches, and when touched it follows you if you attempt to escape from it. By means of it the people defended their walls against Lucullus, and the soldiers were burned in their armor. It is even set on fire in water. We learn by experience that it can be extinguished only by earth.

Naphtha is a substance of a similar nature. It is so called about Babylon and in the territory of the Astaceni in Parthia, flowing like liquid bitumen. It has a great affinity to fire, which instantly darts on it wherever it is seen. It is said that in this way Medea burned Jason's mistress, her crown having taken fire when she approached the altar for the purpose of sacrificing.

Places Which Are Always Burning

Among the wonders of mountains there is Ætna, which always burns in the night, and for so long a period has always had materials for combustion, being in the winter buried in snow, and having the ashes which it has ejected covered with frost. Nor is it in this mountain alone that nature rages, threatening to consume the earth; in Phaselis, the mountain Chimæra burns with a continual flame, day and night. In the same country of Lycia, the mountains of Hephæstius, when touched with a flaming torch, burn so violently that even the stones in the river and the sand burn while actually in the water: this fire is also increased by rain. If a person makes furrows in the ground with a stick which has been kindled at this fire, it is said that a stream of flame will follow it. The summit of Cophantus in Bactria burns during the night; and this is the case in Media and at Sittacene on the borders of Persia; likewise in Susa, at the White Tower, from fifteen apertures, the greatest of which also burns in the daytime. The plain of Babylon throws up flame from a place like a fish pond an acre in extent.

There is also the crater of Nymphæum which is always burning, in the neighborhood of a cold fountain, and which, according to Theopompus, presages direful calamities to the inhabitants of Apollonia. It is increased by rain, and it throws out bitumen which, becoming mixed with the fountain, renders it unfit to be tasted; it is at other times the weakest of all the bitumens. But what are these compared to other wonders? Hiera, one of the Æolian isles in the middle of the sea near Italy, together with the sea itself, during the Social war burned for several days until expiation was made by a deputation from the senate. There is a hill in Ethiopia which burns with the greatest violence, throwing out flame that consumes everything, like the sun. In so many places, and with so many fires, does nature burn the earth!

What must be the nature of that thing which in all parts of the world supplies this most greedy voracity without destroying itself? To these fires must be added those innumerable stars and the great sun itself. There are also the fires made by men, those which are innate in certain kinds of stones, those produced by the friction of wood, and those in the clouds which give rise to lightning. It really exceeds all other wonders that one single day should pass in which everything is not consumed, especially when we reflect that concave mirrors placed opposite to the sun's rays produce flame more readily than any other kind of fire.

Section XVII
THE DEATH OF PLINY

In A.D. 74, Pliny had been appointed by Vespasian præfect of the Roman fleet at Misenum, on the western coast of Italy. It was to this elevation that he owed his romantic death, somewhat similar to that of Empedocles who perished in the crater of Mount Ætna. The closing scene of his active life, simultaneously with the destruction of Herculaneum and Pompeii, cannot be better described than in the language employed by his nephew in an Epistle to his friend Tacitus the historian:

"My uncle was at Misenum, where he was in personal command of the fleet. On the ninth day before the calends of September, at about the seventh hour, 1 P.M., my mother, observing the appearance of a cloud of unusual size and shape, mentioned it to him. After reclining in the sun he had taken his cold bath; he had then again lain down and, after a slight repast, applied himself to his studies. Immediately upon hearing this, he called for his shoes, and ascended a spot from which he could more easily observe this phenomenon. The cloud was to be seen gradually rising upwards; though from the great distance it was uncertain from which of the mountains it arose; it was afterwards, however, ascertained to be Vesuvius. In appearance and shape it strongly resembled a tree; perhaps it was more like a pine than anything else, with a stem of enormous length reaching upwards to the heavens and then spreading out in a number of branches in every direction. I have little doubt that either it had been carried upwards by a violent gust of wind, and that the wind dying away it had lost its compactness, or else that being overcome by its own weight it had decreased in density and become extended over a large surface: at one moment

189

it was white, at another dingy and spotted, just as it was
more or less charged with earth or ashes.

"To a man so eager as he was in the pursuit of knowledge, this appeared to be a most singular phenomenon,
and one that deserved to be viewed more closely; accordingly he gave orders for a light Liburnian vessel to be got
ready, and left it at my option to accompany him. To this
however I made answer, that I should prefer continuing
my studies; and as it happened, he himself had just given
me something to write. Taking his writing tablets with
him, he left the house. The sailors stationed at Retina,
alarmed at the imminence of the danger—for the village
lay at the foot of the mountain, and the sole escape was by
sea—sent to entreat his assistance in rescuing them from
this frightful peril. Upon this he instantly changed his
plans, and what he had already begun from a desire for
knowledge he determined to carry out as a matter of duty.
He had the galleys put to sea at once, and went on board
himself with the intention of rendering assistance, not only
to Retina, but to many other places as well; for the whole
of this charming coast was thickly populated.

Accordingly he made all possible haste towards the
spot from which others were flying, and steered straight
onwards into the very midst of the danger; so far indeed
was he from every sensation of fear that he remarked and
had noted down every movement and every change that
was to be observed in the appearance of this ominous
eruption. The ashes were now falling fast upon the vessels,
hotter and more and more thickly the nearer they approached the shore; showers of pumice intermingled with
black stones, calcined and broken by the action of the
flames: the sea suddenly retreated from the shore, where
the debris of the mountain rendered landing quite impossible. After hesitating for a moment whether or not to turn
back, upon the pilot strongly advising him to do so: "Fortune favors the bold," said he, "conduct me to Pomponianus."

Pomponianus was then at Stabiæ, a place that lay on the other side of the bay, for in those parts the shores are winding, and as they gradually trend away, the sea forms a number of little creeks. At this spot the danger at present was not imminent but still it could be seen, and as it appeared to be approaching nearer and nearer, Pomponianus had ordered his baggage on board the ships, determined to take to flight if the wind, which happened to be blowing the other way, should chance to lull. The wind, being in this quarter, was extremely favorable to his passage, and my uncle soon arriving at Stabiæ, embraced his anxious friend and did his best to restore his courage; and the better to reassure him by evidence of his own sense of their safety he requested the servants to conduct him to the bath. After bathing he took his place at table and dined, and that too in high spirits, or at all events, what equally shows his strength of mind, with every outward appearance of being so.

In the meantime vast sheets of flame and large bodies of fire were to be seen arising from Mount Vesuvius; the glare and brilliancy of which were beheld in bolder relief as the shades of night came on apace. My uncle however, in order to calm their fears, persisted in saying that this was only the light given by some villages which had been abandoned by the rustics, in their alarm, to the flames: after which he retired to rest and soon fell fast asleep: for his respiration, which with him was heavy and loud in consequence of his corpulence, was distinctly heard by the servants who were keeping watch at the door of the apartment. The courtyard which led to his apartment had now become filled with cinders and pumice stones, to such a degree, that if he had remained any longer in the room, it would have been quite impossible for him to leave it. On being awoke he immediately arose, and rejoined Pomponianus and the others who had in the meanwhile been sitting up. They then consulted together whether it would be better to remain in the house or take their chance in the open air; as the building was now rocking to and fro from the violent and repeated shocks, while the walls, as though rooted up from their very foundations, seemed to be at one moment carried in this direction, at another in that.

Having adopted the latter alternative, they were now alarmed at the showers of light calcined pumice stones that were falling thick about them, a risk however to which as a choice of evils they had to submit. In taking this step I must remark that while with my uncle it was reason triumphing over reason, with the rest it was only one fear getting the better of the other. Taking the precaution of placing pillows on their heads, they tied them on with towels by way of protection against the falling stones and ashes. It was now day in other places, though there it was still dark as night, more profound than any ordinary night; torches however and various lights in some measure served to dispel the gloom. It was then determined to make for the shore, and to ascertain whether the sea would now admit of their embarking; it was found however to be still too stormy and too boisterous to allow of their making the attempt. Upon this my uncle lay down on a sail which had been spread for him, and more than once asked for some cold water, which he drank; very soon however they were alarmed by the flames and the sulphurous smell which announced their approach, upon which the others at once took to flight, while my uncle arose leaning upon two of the servants for support. Upon making this effort, he instantly fell to the ground; the dense vapor having, I imagine, stopped the respiration and suffocated him; for his chest was naturally weak and contracted, and often troubled with violent palpitations.

When day was at last restored, the third after the closing one of his existence, his body was found untouched and without a wound; there was no change to be perceived in the clothes, and its appearance was rather that of a person asleep than of a corpse.